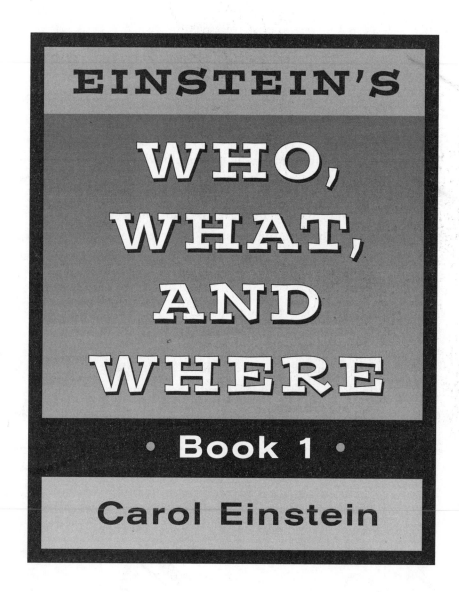

EINSTEIN'S
WHO, WHAT, AND WHERE
· Book 1 ·
Carol Einstein

EDUCATORS PUBLISHING SERVICE
Cambridge and Toronto

To my husband and son, who give me such joy
and who always encourage me to take that extra step.

With thanks and love,
C.S.E.

ACKNOWLEDGMENTS

To Bernice and Herman Einstein who first
encouraged me to take an interest in the world around me.

To my colleagues, friends, and family:
Joan Amron, Mark Donovan, Susanna Einstein, Maureen Farbstein, Marcia Kessler,
Bonnie Long, Jill Mehler, Kathi Ramos, Rosalind Smith, and Jan Sulkowski.
When time is so precious, you were always willing to listen and to help. Thank you.

To my students who told me so frankly what they thought of my ideas and stories.
Your honesty and insights have enriched this book.

With special thanks to my ever skillful editor, Mary Troeger,
who so tactfully clarified my thoughts and who always catches my errors.
Your enthusiasm and true interest in the subject matter are much appreciated.

Cover and book design by Persis Barron Levy

ISBN 0-8388-2651-2
978-0-8388-2651-5
4 5 6 7 MLY 10 09 08 07

Contents

New York City

Dear Reader,

When I was a child, the world seemed much bigger; traveling by airplane was an exciting event. I was a very lucky child. My grandmother lived in Switzerland, and my family would visit her during the summer. After spending time at her home, we would often travel to another country. I loved visiting these new places; they were so different from New York City. As we traveled, my mother always told me wonderful stories about the places we were visiting and the famous events that had happened there. I learned a great deal from these trips. One of the most important things I learned was that the world is full of interesting people, places, and events. I still think this is true, and I'd like to share with you some of these amazing stories.

I hope you enjoy reading them and find them as fascinating as I did.

Carol Einstein

The EMPIRE STATE BUILDING

Think about It....

When you hear the name Empire State Building, what comes to mind?

_____

_____

AS YOU READ Put a ✓ next to parts of the story that you find interesting. Put a **?** next to parts of the story you do not understand.

NOTES

Ask tourists who have visited New York City what one must see, and they will tell you the Empire State Building. People marvel at its beautiful design and its breathtaking views. Yet too few know the amazing story of how the Empire State Building was built.

John J. Raskob and Alfred E. Smith were close friends, and in 1929 both were out of work. Raskob had been a vice president of General Motors, the car company, and was very rich. Smith had been the governor of New York. When he ran for president of the United States in 1928, Raskob left his job to help his friend win the election. But Smith was defeated, so both men were looking for work.

New York needed more office space, but there was only so much land. Smith, a New Yorker, knew that more and more skyscrapers were being built in the city. These tall buildings, whose weight was supported by frames of steel, seemed to be a solution. The New York City skyline with its skyscrapers had replaced the Statue of Liberty as the **symbol** of the city. Smith suggested that Raskob use his money to build one of these giants. Smith, with his New York connections, would be president of the building. Raskob liked the idea and quickly agreed to Smith's plan.

The first drawings showed the Empire State Building with sixty-five stories. Raskob, however, was not satisfied because it was too low. He said that a taller building would make the news and receive lots of free advertising. Either Raskob or the building's architect, William Lamb, pulled out a big pencil, stuck it up in the air, and said that this is what the building should look like.

Raskob had a second reason for wanting the building to be taller. Walter Chrysler, a **rival** in the automobile business, was almost finished with building his own skyscraper in New York City, the Chrysler Building. Raskob wanted to be sure his building was taller than Chrysler's. So Smith announced that their skyscraper would be eighty stories tall and one thousand feet high. This would make it the tallest building in the world.

When Chrysler heard this news, he told his architect to increase the height of his building. In 1930, a stainless steel **spire** was added at the top. It rose like a giant needle into the air, making it 1,048 feet tall. But this was the highest it could go. Nothing more could be added. Raskob was pleased because his building was not yet finished. He could now make his skyscraper taller. The Empire State Building's final height was 1,250 feet, 202 feet taller than the tip of the spire on the Chrysler Building. It had 102 floors with an observation deck on the eighty-sixth floor from which people could see for forty miles.

Not only did the Empire State Building set a record for height, it was also built in record time. When the construction began in March 1930, the country was at the beginning of the Great Depression. Many people were out of work. Workers were eager for any job. About 2,500 people worked on the building each day. From the time the construction began, the frame of the building rose at an average of four-and-a-half floors per week. Once, the workers completed fourteen-and-a-half floors in ten working days.

Cranes lifted big bundles of steel **beams** high up to the top of the unfinished building. To move one of the beams into place, a man stood on it as the crane swung it in the air. With his feet spread apart, the man gripped a steel rope for support. While the beam was in the air, the worker turned it with his feet until the steel unit was at just the right angle. Then the crane lowered it into place. People on the street below stood three and four deep, watching the steelworkers construct the building. They said that the men reminded them of acrobats. A magazine writer compared the workers to little spiders spinning a fabric of steel against the sky.

As the building rose story by story, a tiny railroad was built on each level to carry needed supplies. At its busiest, there were about three thousand men working at one time. When the workers complained that they were late getting back from lunch because they could not find a place to eat, movable cafeterias were built on the

scaffolding. As the building increased in height, more were added. Finally, cafeterias were on the third, the ninth, the twenty-fourth, the forty-seventh, and the sixty-fourth floors. For forty cents, a worker could buy a hot meal or a couple of sandwiches, something to drink, and a piece of pie. Ten miles of water pipes carried drinking water to the workers.

In the early 1930s, there was little safety equipment. Since the work was so dangerous, a nurse worked full-time, and a doctor visited several times a day. An entrance to the building site was always kept free in case an ambulance was needed.

The building took one year and forty-five days to build. This is still a record for building a skyscraper of such a height. As soon as the Empire State Building went up, people loved it. From the time it opened, many tourists visited the observation decks and were thrilled by the marvelous views. The building became an instant symbol of New York City. Many people believe it is the city's and the world's greatest skyscraper.

symbol – something that stands for or represents something else

rival – a person who tries to be as good as or better than another

spire – a tall, narrow structure that tapers to a point at the top

beam – a long, strong piece of wood or metal, used in buildings for support

scaffolding – a group of platforms for workers to stand on as they work high above the ground on a building

LOOKING BACK AT WHAT YOU HAVE READ

Write your answers to the following questions on the lines below. When the question is in bold print, underline the answer in the story, and write the number of the question in the margin. The answer may be in more than one place. Then write it below.

1. **Why did Smith suggest to Raskob that he build a large skyscraper?**

   _____

   _____

2. Why did Raskob want to have the tallest building in New York City?

   _____

   _____

   _____

3. **How tall is the Empire State Building?**

   _____

   _____

4. Why do you think there was often a large crowd watching as the building went up?

   _____

   _____

   _____

5. **Why were people glad to be working on the Empire State Building?**

   _____

   _____

6. What are some other famous skyscrapers?

   _____

   _____

WORKING WITH WORDS

🌀 What three new words did you learn from this story?

_____   _____   _____

Try to use two of them in sentences.

_____

_____

_____

> A **proverb** is a short saying that expresses something that many people
> believe to be true. "Birds of a feather flock together" is a proverb.
> It means that people who have the same interests and beliefs
> are drawn to each other.

🌀 Explain how the building of the Empire State Building is an example of the proverb
"Many hands make light work."

_____

_____

_____

🌀 Explain how Governor Al Smith's actions after losing the election are an example of
the proverb "Don't cry over spilled milk."

_____

_____

_____

Sometimes words have more than one meaning.

Example: The waiter gave me the **bill**.

In the sentence, *bill* means the piece of paper that tells you how much you owe. *Bill* can also mean the beak of a bird.

In the following sentences, the word in bold print has one meaning. Write what it is. Then see if you can write another meaning the word may have.

Raskob and Smith were **close** friends.

_____

_____

_____

The spire **rose** like a giant needle.

_____

_____

_____

It was 202 feet taller than the **tip** of the spire on the Chrysler Building.

_____

_____

_____

WRITING SKILLS

Write a summary of the story. Do not forget to include the important events. After you have written your summary, be sure to proofread it. Check your spelling, grammar, punctuation, and capitalization. Then meet in a group with other students and share your summaries.

_____

_____

_____

_____

_____

_____

_____

_____

_____

_____

_____

_____

_____

_____

_____

_____

_____

Pretend you are John Raskob. You are writing in your diary, describing the opening of the Empire State Building. Write down what you did on that day and what you thought. When you have finished your writing, proofread it. Check it for correct spelling, grammar, capitalization, and punctuation.

Conquering MOUNT EVEREST

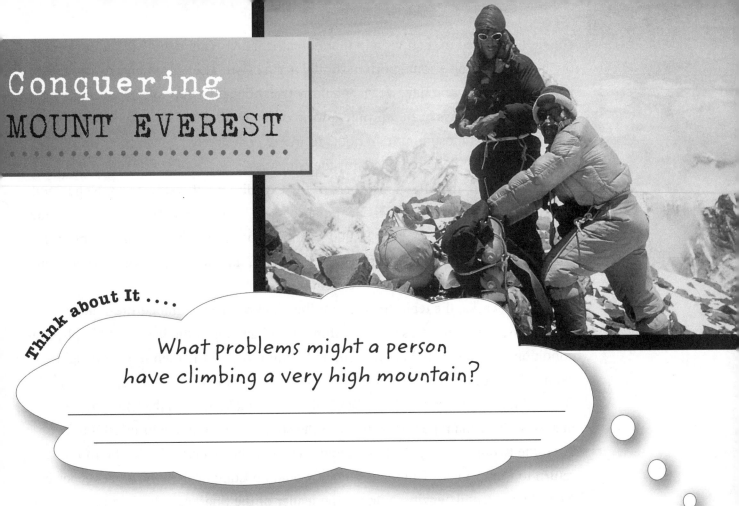

Think about It . . . .

What problems might a person
have climbing a very high mountain?

_____

_____

AS YOU READ Put a ★ beside two important ideas in the story. Then write in the margin why each idea is important.

NOTES

Starting in 1921, groups of mountain climbers had been trying to reach the **summit** of Mount Everest, the highest mountain in the world. Set in the Himalaya Mountains of Nepal, Mount Everest, or Chomolungma as it is called in Tibetan, is 29,028 feet tall. Seven major **expeditions**, all with outstanding, well-equipped mountain climbers, tried to reach the summit, but none made it to the top. Many climbers died high on the mountain in the ice and snow.

What makes Everest so dangerous is the great height. There is less oxygen the higher one goes. Climbers become worn out. Their muscles, nerves, and mind weaken quickly as the oxygen decreases. Just as they must face the mountain's most difficult climbing conditions, they have the least oxygen. One person, who tried to climb Everest, described it this way, "On Everest it is an effort to cook, an effort to talk, an effort to think, almost too much of an effort to live."

In 1953, an expedition from Great Britain tried to reach the summit of Mount Everest. Colonel John Hunt, a British army officer and a skilled climber, was the leader. When planning the expedition, he felt his most important job was to choose the right climbers, men who had energy and drive as well as team spirit. He also knew how important it was to pick the best equipment. On earlier attempts, some climbers had used oxygen to help them breathe. Now Hunt decided that not only the climbers but also some porters should use oxygen. The cotton and nylon tents, which were made of a new weave, could withstand gales of up to 100 miles per hour. Footwear had always been a problem for mountain climbers. The smallest amount of moisture caused most mountain boots to freeze completely. So the climbers received two sets of newly designed boots for the trip.

On March 10, the fifteen members of the expedition left Kathmandu, Nepal, and walked about 180 miles to their headquarters at Thyangboche. With them were 362 porters, 20 Sherpa guides, and 10,000 pounds of baggage. The Sherpa, the people who live on the southern slopes of the Himalayas, had been on all the earlier Mount Everest expeditions. They were excellent guides.

For two weeks, the team traveled up the **glaciers**. They climbed the smaller mountains, trying to get used to the thin air and getting in the best possible physical condition. Starting at 17,900 feet, Colonel Hunt directed the men to set up eight camps. Then he chose two teams of climbers. Charles Evans, a doctor, and Tom Bourdillon, a scientist, would be the first team to make the climb. They had two missions. Their main goal was to get to the south summit, a height of 28,700 feet. Then the two men would have to decide whether they should try for the top or return to Camp Eight. The second team would be Edmond Hillary, a beekeeper from New Zealand, and Tenzing Norgay, the leader of the Sherpas, who had made more attempts on Everest than any other living man. If the first team failed, the second would try to reach the summit of Mount Everest.

On May 26, Bourdillon and Evans started climbing up from Camp Eight, which was 3,200 feet from the top, toward a rounded shoulder of rock. When they were only three hundred feet below the summit of Everest they had to turn back. There was not enough time to reach the top and also return to camp before dark. Already exhausted, they fell several times, including once from the top to the bottom of a great **gully**. It was a miracle they survived. Bourdillon was very disappointed they had not tried for the top, but Evans knew they never would have returned.

On May 27, the weather was bad, and Colonel Hunt decided that the second team should not climb until conditions improved. Hunt, Bourdillon, Evans, and a porter returned to Camp Seven.

The next day, Hillary and Norgay were ready for their turn. Hunt's instructions to Hillary were: "Don't give in, but get back." Hillary and Norgay left the camp with two other climbers, Al Gregory and George Lowe, and a porter. Trying to save Hillary's and Norgay's strength for their final climb, Gregory and Lowe cut steps into the ice to the place where Hillary and Norgay would spend the night. Then Gregory, Lowe, and the porter returned to Camp Eight. Chopping out frozen **rubble** with their ice axes, Hillary and Norgay cleared a spot large enough for their tent, but it was on two levels. Through the night, the tent was hit by frequent, fierce gusts of wind. Using a heater to warm some liquids, the two men drank lots of sweet lemon water, soup, and coffee. They ate sardines on biscuits, a tin of apricots, and biscuits with jam.

On May 29, they awoke early. It was seventeen degrees below zero, with a clear sky and hardly any wind. In spite of the new design, their boots had frozen solid during the night. With the stove between his knees, Hillary started cooking the boots. Although they ended up slightly burned, the boots were soft enough to put on. Hillary and Norgay dressed in all the clothes they had, including three pairs of gloves.

At 6:30 A.M., Hillary and Norgay connected the oxygen to their face masks, tied on their nylon rope, which linked them together, and grasped their ice axes. The climbing was very dangerous. Whenever Hillary felt afraid, he would say to himself, "Forget it! This is Everest and you've got to take a few risks." Norgay said that he did not like it, but he did not suggest going back.

At 9 A.M., they reached the south summit where Bordillon and Evans were forced to turn back. Hillary and Norgay cut steps in the hard, frozen snow and climbed the bumps and overhanging masses of ice, looking for the summit. They felt that it was impossible to tell which bump was the top of Everest. Finally, Hillary climbed up a gentle snow ridge. Clearly, this was the top! Hillary recalled, "Suddenly I realize that the ridge ahead doesn't slope up, but down. I look quickly to my right. There, just above me, is a softly rounded, snow-covered little bump about as big as a haystack. The summit."

He waved to Norgay to come up. A few more whacks of the ice ax, a few more very tired steps, and the two men were on the summit. It was 11:30 A.M. Hillary recalled that he felt relief that this long, hard job was over and that they had reached the summit before their oxygen supplies became dangerously low. He was somewhat surprised that of all the brave, determined climbers, he and Norgay were the ones to reach the top. The two men shook hands. Then Norgay threw his arm around Hillary's shoulders, and they thumped each other on the back.

But the two did not have a moment to lose. They had to take some pictures and then climb down before their oxygen ran out. Hillary photographed Norgay and then took photos in every direction. Norgay, a Buddhist, scratched out a little hole in the snow and put in it a small offering to the gods of Chomolungma, which all religious Buddhists believe live on the summit. Near these gifts, Hillary put a little cross that Hunt had given him.

After staying only fifteen minutes, the two men started down. What did it feel like to be there? "Damn good!" said Hillary. "I thought of God and the greatness of the world," said Norgay. Twenty years later, looking back on their climb, Hillary said, "We were a good team, of that I am convinced. We shared the work, the risks, and the success; it was a team effort and nothing else is important."

summit – the highest point of a mountain

expedition – a long journey made for a particular reason

glacier – a large mass of ice in very cold regions or on the tops of high mountains

gully – a narrow ditch made by flowing water

rubble – rough, broken pieces of stone, rock, or other solid materials

LOOKING BACK AT WHAT YOU HAVE READ

✺ Write your answers to the following questions on the lines below. When the question is in bold print, underline the answer in the story, and write the number of the question in the margin. The answer may be in more than one place. Then write it below.

1. **Why is it difficult to climb Mount Everest?**

_____

_____

_____

2. **Why were the Sherpa guides so useful?**

_____

_____

3. Why do you think a person would want to climb Mount Everest?

_____

_____

4. Do you think Colonel Hunt was a good leader? Give reasons for your answers.

_____

_____

_____

5. Why do you think earlier expeditions failed?

_____

_____

_____

6. If you were the first person to climb Mount Everest, what would you do when you reached the summit?

_____

_____

_____

WORKING WITH WORDS

◉ How many describing words can you think of that tell what the climb to the summit of Mount Everest was like? See if you can think of at least three.

_____   _____   _____

_____   _____   _____

> Did you know that some words sound alike but are spelled differently and have different meanings? These words are called **homophones**.
>
> Example: *ant* and *aunt*
> An *ant* crawled along the edge of the counter.
> My *aunt* talks to my mother once a week.

◉ See if you can fill in the blanks with homophones. Be sure to read all the sentences in each group before you write your answers.

Mount Everest is a very high _____.

The children were told not to _____ into the closet where the birthday gift was hidden.

Some of the climbing equipment was made of _____.

I hope no one tries to _____ my bicycle.

The climbers waited _____ the day for the weather to improve.

My father _____ me the ball.

When people _____ that climbers had reached the summit of Mount Everest, they were amazed.

The _____ of mountain goats watched us from a snowy ledge.

After Hillary and Norgay reached the summit, everyone on the expedition felt a
_____ sense of pride.

Where is your fishing rod and _____?

Hillary and Norgay grasped _____ ice axes.

_____ supposed to be away for two weeks.

_____ are two birds in the tree.

A **suffix** is a letter or group of letters that we place at the end of a word
or word root to change its meaning. The suffix *-ful* means "full of."

Example: *playful*

Peter likes to *play*. He is a very *playful* child.

◎ List three words and then make new words by adding the suffix *-ful*.

care   **careful**

_____   _____

_____   _____

_____   _____

◎ The suffix *-able* means "possible to." List three words and then make new words by adding
the suffix *-able*.

agree   **agreeable**

_____   _____

_____   _____

_____   _____

WRITING SKILLS

You are about to climb a big mountain with a group of friends. Write a letter to either Hillary or Norgay, asking for advice about how you can prepare for the trip. Write down some key ideas. When you finish the letter, proofread it. Remember to check for correct spelling, grammar, capitalization, and punctuation.

Key ideas

- _____
- _____
- _____

Dear _____,

_____

_____

_____

_____

_____

_____

_____

_____

_____

Sincerely,

_____

Pretend you are Norgay or Hillary and write a letter back. Be sure to include a list of items that a climber must have and a list of items that would be nice to have but are not necessary. Before you begin your letter, write down some key ideas. When you finish the letter, proofread it. Remember to check for correct spelling, grammar, capitalization, and punctuation.

Key ideas

- _____
- _____
- _____

Dear _____,

_____

_____

_____

_____

_____

_____

_____

_____

_____

_____

_____

Yours truly,

_____

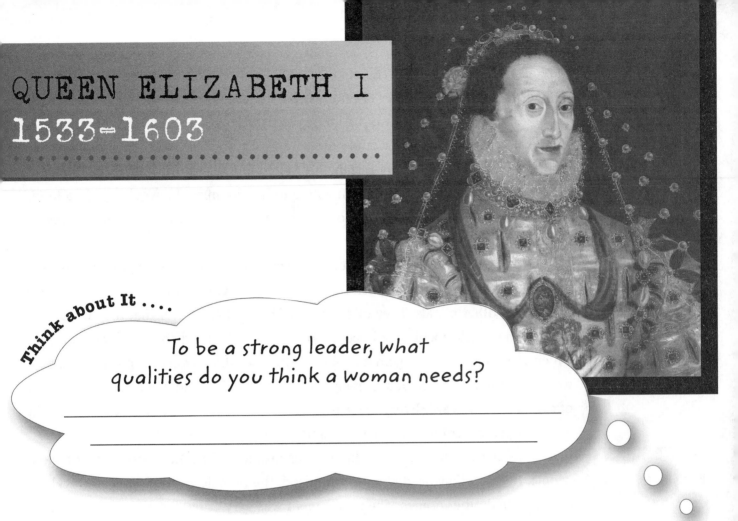

QUEEN ELIZABETH I
1533–1603

To be a strong leader, what qualities do you think a woman needs?

_____

_____

AS YOU READ Put a ✓ next to parts of the story that you find interesting. Put a **?** next to parts of the story you do not understand.

NOTES

At a time when governing was considered "a masculine business" and people believed it was unnatural for a woman to rule men, twenty-five-year-old Elizabeth, a single woman, became queen of England. At first, everyone thought that she would marry, that her husband would rule, that she would have a son, and that later he would rule. But Elizabeth never married. When she began her reign, she told her people that she would be as good to them as any queen had ever been to her subjects. She said, "My care is for my people."

Elizabeth enjoyed ruling and believed that she could be a good queen. She chose her advisors carefully and often asked for their opinions. However, she was the one who decided what to do. The queen expected full obedience from the people advising her. Rather than forcing them to obey her, she preferred charming them into agreeing with her. To make sure that they did not take their jobs for granted, Elizabeth would change the way she treated people. Sometimes she quickly got angry with them, and at other times she was warm and kind.

England was in very bad shape when Elizabeth became queen. There were religious problems. Her father, Henry VIII, had left the Catholic Church and started the Protestant Church of England. This upset Catholics in England and in Europe. There were also money problems. The country was almost broke, and people's money was not worth much. The number of poor people increased. Elizabeth knew that if there was a war, she would not have the money to fight it. Besides, she did not want to share her power, which she would have to do with any man that she chose to lead her troops. So for many years Elizabeth disliked and feared war. Whenever she and her advisors talked about a problem with another country, she would say in a loud, commanding voice, "No war, my Lords! No war!" Over several years, this **policy** helped England recover.

Queen Elizabeth wanted to correct the things that were wrong with her kingdom. She began with the money, which had lost its value. Gold and silver coins had been mixed with other metals. They had only half the gold and silver that they were supposed to have. Elizabeth asked people to exchange their old coins for new ones, which were made of pure gold and silver. Although these coins were smaller, they were worth more. To encourage people to exchange their old coins, the government offered a small reward. Everyone was so eager to do as the queen asked that within a year England's coins were as good as those of any other country.

Then Elizabeth turned to another serious problem, England's poor and homeless people. Because they needed money for food, the homeless rioted, robbed travelers, or committed other crimes. The punishment was very cruel. People were hanged, often fifty or more people at one time. Elizabeth knew this was not an answer and set up a committee to look into the matter. They came up with a group of new laws to help the poor.

As the years passed under Elizabeth's rule, England **prospered**. There was so much fine wool and linen cloth to **export** that more ships were built. New companies formed and asked the queen for permission to trade. For centuries, all the trading had been done in an eastward direction with Europe and Asia. When the lands of the Americas were discovered, England wanted to open new routes to the West for buying and selling. King Philip of Spain, however, controlled that trade. Elizabeth encouraged her sea captains to explore other sea routes. During the 1570s, England opened trade routes with Russia.

Sometimes, daring English sea captains sailed on the Atlantic. Whenever they met Spanish trading ships, a fight began. If the English won, they seized the goods carried by ship and made the Spanish sailors their prisoners. If they lost, the Spanish took their cargo and made them prisoners. Neither Queen Elizabeth nor most of her subjects considered this wrong.

In 1577 with the queen's support, Francis Drake, a sea captain, put together a **fleet** of five ships and headed for South America. Along the way, Drake captured Spanish ships and robbed Spanish settlements. After a three-year voyage around the world, he returned to England with enormous loot. He gave Elizabeth half of it; this was worth a huge amount.

Protestant England and Catholic Spain never forgot their disagreement about religion, and as time went on, a hatred grew. It reached its **peak** when Philip was suspected of plotting to get rid of Elizabeth so that he could put a Catholic on the English throne.

Spain was a more powerful country than England. Finally, Philip decided he would try to conquer England. He had the largest and strongest fleet in the world, the Spanish *Armada*. With 114 ships carrying 19,000 soldiers and 8,000 sailors, he was sure he would win any battle. In 1588, the *Armada* sailed for England.

Queen Elizabeth went to review her troops along the coast, who were ready to drive back the Spanish if they tried to land. Mounted on a white horse, Elizabeth rode through the cheering soldiers. Then she spoke to them. "I know I have the body of a weak and feeble woman. But I have the heart of a king, and of a king of England, too. I myself will take up arms!" When they heard these words, her troops felt great love and respect for their queen. Before the Spanish *Armada* could land, the English fleet defeated it.

Although the war with Spain continued for sixteen more years, English ships ruled the seas. The English could trade with whomever they wanted. They explored new worlds, including America, where they claimed land for England and started colonies.

Elizabeth was always very interested in the arts. During her rule, she supported musicians and spent large amounts of money to have concerts and plays presented at her court. She provided free concerts for her subjects. She, too, played and composed music. During Elizabeth's reign, some of the world's greatest plays and poems were written. William Shakespeare, the great playwright, often presented his plays at Elizabeth's court. For forty-five years, Queen Elizabeth ruled England. When she died at the age of seventy, few of her subjects could remember a time without her.

policy - a guiding belief or plan that people use to help them make decisions

prosper - to do well, to be successful

export - to send goods to other countries to sell or trade

fleet - a group of warships under one command; a group of ships, airplanes, or cars

peak - the highest point or greatest level

LOOKING BACK AT WHAT YOU HAVE READ

Write your answers to the following questions on the lines below. When the question is in bold print, underline the answer in the story, and write the number of the question in the margin. The answer may be in more than one place. Then write it below.

1. Why was Queen Elizabeth such an outstanding queen?

_____

_____

_____

2. **What was the main disagreement between England and Spain?**

_____

_____

_____

3. Why do you think people in Queen Elizabeth's time thought it was not natural for a woman to rule?

_____

_____

_____

4. Why do you think Queen Elizabeth never married?

_____

_____

5. Do you think that Queen Elizabeth should have made Drake return his loot to Spain? Explain your answer.

_____

_____

6. How did Queen Elizabeth support the arts?

_____

_____

_____

WORKING WITH WORDS

Word Puzzle

◎ Using the letters in the word *Elizabeth*, see how many small words you can make. You may use a letter twice in your word if it appears twice in this name.

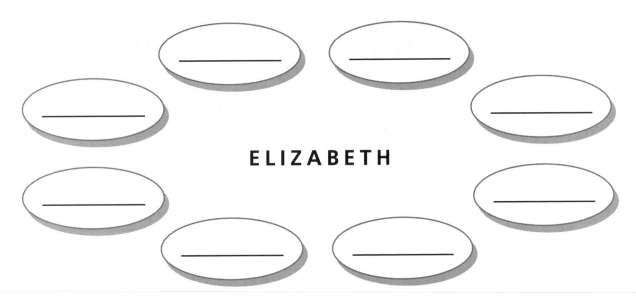

ELIZABETH

Do you know that an **idiom** is a group of words that have a special meaning? If you do not know the special meaning, you will not understand what a person is saying. In fact, it may sound very silly.

For example, "To put your foot into your mouth." This means to say the wrong thing to someone.

◎ Read the explanations of the following idioms. Then write your own sentence using the idioms. Be sure to give yourself a bonus point if you can do the last one.

The idiom "walking on air" means to be very happy.
When Queen Elizabeth heard of Drake's loot, she was walking on air.

_____

_____

"To play second fiddle" means having a less important job or position.

Queen Elizabeth never married because she knew if she did, she would have to play second fiddle to her husband.

_____

_____

The idiom "pulling the rug out from under him" means to unexpectedly spoil his plans.

When the English defeated the Spanish fleet, King Philip felt as though the rug was pulled out from under him.

BONUS
POINT

_____

_____

As you know, a **definition** explains the meaning of a word or group of words. A definition of the word *herd* is a group of animals that live or travel together.

Write a definition for the following words.

govern

_____

_____

advisor

_____

_____

encourage

_____

_____

daring

_____

_____

loot

_____

_____

WRITING SKILLS

In 1603 Queen Elizabeth died. Pretend you are a princess or a prince, and you are asked to speak at her funeral. You want to talk about why Elizabeth was such a great queen. You are afraid you will get nervous, so you write down what you are going to say.

First, write down some key ideas. When you have finished your paragraph, remember to proofread your writing. Check it for correct spelling, grammar, capitalization, and punctuation.

Key ideas

🔑 _____

🔑 _____

🔑 _____

Speech

_____

_____

_____

_____

_____

_____

_____

_____

_____

_____

_____

_____

_____

_____

_____

Many of Queen Elizabeth's subjects thought she was an outstanding queen and liked her very much. Write a paragraph about a person that you like. Be sure that your paragraph has a title, a topic sentence, which gives the main idea of the paragraph, and a concluding sentence, which lets the reader know that you have finished your discussion.

First, write down some key ideas. When you have finished your paragraph, remember to proofread your writing. Check it for correct spelling, grammar, capitalization, and punctuation.

Key ideas

Title:

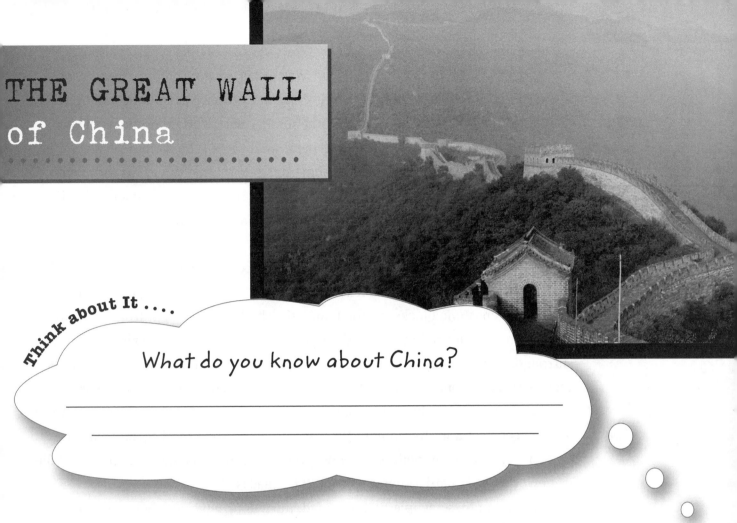

THE GREAT WALL of China

What do you know about China?

_____

_____

AS YOU READ Put a ★ beside two important ideas in the story. Then write in the margin why each idea is important.

Built more than two thousand years ago, the Great Wall extends for about two thousand miles, but with its branches and loops, its length totals nearly four thousand miles. There is nothing else like it in the world.

After Qin Shihuandgi united six Chinese states in 221 B.C. and became the "First Emperor" of China, he had to protect his people against attacks by **barbarian** tribes in the north. These tribes lived by hunting and kidnapping people, whom they made into slaves. Emperor Qin had to make sure that the Chinese **border**, which was almost two thousand miles long, could be defended. He decided to build a wall, which would become the greatest one ever built. Earlier, the Chinese states of Qin, Yan, and Zhao had built walls to separate themselves from their neighbors. Qin's wall would connect and strengthen these walls. The emperor said that his wall would be "the most warlike barrier in the world." This great but cruel warrior wanted his empire to last "for ten thousand generations," and he knew that for this to happen he would have to keep his barbarian neighbors out.

Qin had at his command a huge army, **peasants** he had recently freed, and many prisoners. If they were needed, all of these people could help build the wall.

The emperor chose General Meng T'ien, one of his greatest military leaders, to be in charge of the project. Three hundred thousand people slaved under the general's command, but it is believed that the total number who worked on the wall was far greater, probably over a million. The general used those who were serving time in jail, those who spoke out against the emperor's harsh laws, as well as those who were captured during Chinese wars. Besides men, thousands of women helped with the building. Some of them carried stones and bricks and others wove canvas for tents.

The emperor and his general showed little concern for the workers. They had to cut rock, drag stone, make bricks, and pound clay. The working conditions were terrible. Often, stone blocks for the foundation had to be brought from far away. The clay needed for filling the inside of the wall was not always available in the surrounding area. Armies of workers had to carry the needed material in baskets that were slung from each end of a pole resting on their shoulders. The work continued year round through all kinds of weather. In the winter, there were freezing gusts of snow, and in the summer there were such terrible sandstorms that the workers' eyes were blinded. No one was allowed to rest. As men collapsed and died from working too hard, other men took their places.

Since all of these people had to be fed, thirty-four huge supply bases were built near the work area. Whenever it was possible, the land near the wall was used to grow food for the workers. But often, not enough could be produced in one place; so more had to be brought in from other parts of China. The Chinese who were not building the wall also had to work very hard. They were forced to raise all the food that was needed to feed the rest of the country.

The cost of constructing the wall was very high. To raise money, the emperor made his people pay heavy taxes. With such killing work and high taxes, the Chinese people suffered a great deal. One person cried out, "If you have a son, get rid of him. If you have a daughter, drown her! Do you not see, at the foot of the Great Wall the piles of dead bodies on which it is built?"

Qin's wall took about twelve years to build. When it was finished, it was what he had wanted, "a most warlike barrier." On the outside edge, there were **battlements**. Along both sides were watchtowers. These allowed the soldiers to look for enemies and to shoot at them. Using smoke signals during the day and fires at night, the soldiers could warn people if there was an emergency,

Besides protecting the country, the wall also served as a major highway. It had an average height of twenty-four feet and was wide enough for five horsemen to ride side by side on its top. Soldiers could march by columns of ten. In mountainous areas that would be very difficult to cross on land, Qin could quickly move his soldiers with their equipment great distances. For a person traveling the length of the wall by horse, it would take at least a month. During this journey the traveler would cross **plains**, rivers, valleys, and mountains. After Qin's death, some Chinese rulers allowed the wall to crumble while others strengthened it. Today, the Chinese government is once again fixing parts of the Great Wall. For the Chinese people, this amazing structure represents a part of their long history. For visitors from around the world, it is one important reason to go to China.

barbarian – a person that belongs to a culture or people that is believed by another culture to be savage or uncivilized

border – the dividing line where one country or area ends and another begins; a boundary

peasant – long ago, a person who worked on a farm or owned a small farm

battlement – a low wall built along the top of a fort or tower

plain – a large area of flat or almost flat land

LOOKING BACK AT WHAT YOU HAVE READ

Write your answers to the following questions on the lines below. When the question is in bold print, underline the answer in the story, and write the number of the question in the margin. The answer may be in more than one place. Then write it below.

1. When was the Great Wall built?

_____

_____

2. **Why was the Great Wall built?**

_____

_____

_____

3. Do you think the wall alone would be enough to keep the barbarians out? Explain your answer.

_____

_____

4. **In addition to keeping the barbarians out, how else was the wall used?**

_____

_____

5. The Chinese people suffered great pain while building the wall. Do you think the wall was worth it? Explain your answer.

_____

_____

_____

6. Besides building a wall, how can a country stop people from entering?

_____

_____

_____

WORKING WITH WORDS

Look at the words in white. Then look at the pairs of words below them. The words in white explain the relationship between those pairs. Can you write three additional pairs for each item?

opposites	structure and location
cruel–kind	the Great Wall–China

whole to part	part to whole
wall–bricks	handle–basket

Do you remember that a **prefix** is a letter or group of letters that we place at the beginning of a word or word root to change the meaning? The prefix *dis-* means "not" or "opposite."

Example: *discontinue*
The store *discontinued* selling my favorite brand of ice cream.

List three words and then make new words by adding the prefix *dis-*.

arm   disarm

_____   _____

_____   _____

_____   _____

⊚ The prefix *over-* means "too much." Try to list three words and then make new words by adding the prefix *over-*.

active   **overactive**

_____   _____

_____   _____

_____   _____

> What do you think a **synonym** is? It is a word that has the same or almost the same meaning as another word. A *parcel* and a *package* are synonyms.

⊚ Think of synonyms for the words that follow. See if you can write two.

protect   _____   _____

terrible   _____   _____

quickly   _____   _____

huge   _____   _____

connect   _____   _____

cruel   _____   _____

WRITING SKILLS

Draw pictures showing four important parts of the story about building the Great Wall of China. Then write about each picture.

_____
_____
_____
_____

_____
_____
_____
_____

_____
_____
_____
_____

_____
_____
_____
_____

Imagine you are a travel reporter writing about how amazing the Great Wall is. Your paragraph about the wall will be published in a travel magazine. Be sure that your paragraph has a title, a topic sentence, which gives the main idea of the paragraph, and a concluding sentence, which lets the reader know that you have finished your discussion.

First, write down some key ideas. When you have finished your paragraph, proofread your writing. Check it for correct spelling, grammar, capitalization, and punctuation.

Key ideas

- _____
- _____
- _____

Title:

_____

_____

_____

_____

_____

_____

_____

_____

_____

_____

_____

_____

_____

_____

_____

_____

_____

_____

_____

Banning DDT

What do you do to
protect the world around you?

_____

_____

AS YOU READ Put a ✓ next to parts of the story that you find interesting. Put a **?**
next to parts of the story you do not understand.

OTES

Rarely does one book have a large effect nationwide, but that is exactly what happened when Rachel Carson's *Silent Spring* was published. Carson, a scientist and well-known science writer charged that the chemical business, the farming business, and the government were using **pesticides** without knowing what effect they might have on people and nature. Arguing that these chemicals were entering our food and water, Carson wrote that they should be carefully controlled. Because of *Silent Spring,* people demanded that the government protect people's health and establish rules for any actions that affected the environment.

In 1958, a friend of Carson's, Olga Huckins, wrote to her. Huckins had a private bird **sanctuary** on her property in Duxbury, Massachusetts. She told Carson how the state of Massachusetts had **conducted** an aerial spraying program against mosquitoes by covering the area with a mixture of DDT and fuel oil. The fuel oil made the DDT stick to whatever it was sprayed on. The results were shocking—large numbers of birds and insects died. Huckins described how the mosquitoes that survived were the hungriest she had ever seen, while the grasshoppers, bees, and other harmless insects were all gone. Huckins asked Carson to find someone in Washington who might help her with this problem.

Carson had worked for fifteen years as a writer and editor for the U.S. Fish and Wildlife Service in Washington, D.C. Besides having a home in Maine, she still spent part of each year in Silver Spring, Maryland, near Washington. As she began to search for information and learned more about the use of pesticides, she became very upset. She discovered that aerial spraying was taking place all over the country. No one, however, was looking at what the long-lasting effects might be on people and the environment. In New York, a group of people planned to go to court to stop the spraying of pesticides. In 1957, DDT had been sprayed over a large area to kill gypsy moths, which were damaging the trees. Instead, it destroyed flowers and shrubs, damaged cars, and killed many insects, birds, and even a horse.

Carson said, "I realized that here was material for a book. What I discovered was that everything which meant most to me as a **naturalist** was being threatened, and that nothing I could do would be more important." Carson spent four-and-a-half years writing *Silent Spring*.

When DDT was first used in the early 1940s, during World War II, it was considered a wonderful invention. It could protect United States soldiers by killing the insects that carry malaria, a deadly disease. In the late 1940s, after the war was over, more and more DDT was produced. It became a big business for those who made it, earning them millions of dollars in profits every year. Farmers, too, were delighted because it protected their crops.

But Carson told her readers a different story about pesticides. She said the new chemicals were dangerous. They were deadly to harmful insects, but they also killed insects that helped humans. Because pesticides were sprayed, the chemicals were in the air that people breathed. They soaked into the ground when it rained or snowed. What was left on the plants and in the earth found its way into the water that people drank. The chemicals ran into rivers, where they killed fish. In time, they ended up in the oceans and affected the plants and animals living there. Carson's point was that these chemicals, "have the power to kill every insect, the 'good' and the 'bad,' to still the song of birds and the leaping of fish in the streams" even though the target may be only a few weeds or insects. In the last chapter of her book, Carson suggested that a safe way to control pests would be to use a combination of methods. While this approach would be more expensive and complicated, it would be much safer.

Even before *Silent Spring* came out, people were talking about it. Two parts were published in the *New Yorker* in 1962, and the magazine received a record number of letters. Most readers wrote to say how glad they were that Carson had **exposed** the problem. Many readers expressed anger at the government for using such a large amount of pesticide. The *New Yorker* articles impressed President Kennedy, too, who told his science advisor to look into the problem.

As soon as the book was published, it became a best seller. People across the country began to ask questions. Realizing it might lose business, the chemical industry tried to convince people that Carson was a crazy woman who did not know what she was talking about.

Before long, a popular television news program, *CBS Reports*, decided to air a special program to discuss the spraying of pesticides. Ten to fifteen million people watched as Eric Sevareid, a well-known news reporter, opened the show by saying that there was a pesticide problem. Sevareid told his viewers that Carson thought there should be a slow change to other ways of pest control. Then Carson was interviewed; she explained the effects of pesticides. A man speaking for the chemical business tried to scare people by arguing that human survival would be in danger without chemicals. Many important government witnesses were also on the show. Listening to them, viewers concluded that few in the government seemed to know very much about the chemicals or their effects. This was exactly what Carson had said in *Silent Spring*.

The day after the television show, the United States Senate formed a committee to look into environmental problems, including the use of pesticides. People realized that they needed to do something about the problem themselves, so they formed groups that started working to protect the environment.

On June 8, 1963, Carson appeared before the Senate committee. The room was packed; television cameras were set up so people nationwide could hear her. Carson spoke calmly. "The problem you have chosen to explore is one that must be solved in our time. I feel strongly that a beginning must be made on it now." She added that spraying pesticides from airplanes should be brought under strict control. The amount of pesticide used should be reduced to the lowest strength needed for the job. Then, as soon as possible, the use of pesticides should end. Carson said that people had the right to be safe in their own homes, protected against poison applied by other people.

As she neared the end of writing *Silent Spring*, Carson wrote to a good friend saying that she felt a serious duty to do what she could to save the living world. "If I didn't at least try I could never again be happy in nature. But now I can believe I have at least helped a little." Carson's book led to stricter rules about the use of pesticides and made people realize that the environment had to be protected. Nine years later, the use of DDT was banned in the United States.

pesticide – a chemical used to kill insects, mice, and other animal pests

sanctuary – a natural area where birds and animals are protected

conduct – to manage or carry out

naturalist – a person who specializes in the study of things in nature; especially animals and plants

expose – to make something known; to reveal

LOOKING BACK AT WHAT YOU HAVE READ

Write your answers to the following questions on the lines below. When the question is in bold print, underline the answer in the story, and write the number of the question in the margin. The answer may be in more than one place. Then write it below.

1. **What happened when large amounts of pesticides were sprayed?**

_____

_____

_____

2. Why was *Silent Spring* such an important book?

_____

_____

_____

3. **Why did Carson begin writing *Silent Spring*?**

_____

_____

_____

4. **What was the result of the two *New Yorker* articles?**

_____

_____

_____

5. Why was the *CBS Reports* program on pesticides so important?

_____

_____

_____

6. Is there ever a time when you think poisonous chemicals should be used? Explain your answer.

_____

_____

_____

WORKING WITH WORDS

When people read *Silent Spring*, many thought it was a wonderful and important book. Think of a favorite book of yours. Write down its name and then list as many describing words as you can, telling what it was like. See if you can think of at least four.

Name of book: _____

_____   _____   _____

_____   _____   _____

> Have you ever heard of a **simile**? A simile is a phrase or expression introduced by the words *like* or *as*. It compares two things that are not alike.
>
> **Example:** As Carson learned more about pesticides, she became *as mad as a hornet.*

Explain what the simile above means. Then see if you can use it in a sentence.

_____

_____

_____

Now try to explain what these similes mean and see if you can use them in sentences. Give yourself a bonus point if you can do the last one.

Carson worked *like a dog* when she wrote *Silent Spring*.

_____

_____

_____

After reading her book, many people thought Carson was *as smart as a whip*.

_____

_____

_____

Knowing that she had helped save the living world, Carson felt *as light as a feather*.

_____

_____

_____

🌀 How are a knife, a saw, and a razor alike? If you said that they are all blades, you are correct. Now read the following sets of words and explain how they are alike.

| wand | rabbit | hats | cards |

_____

_____

| silver | iron | gold | copper |

_____

_____

| brook | river | pond | stream |

_____

_____

| ounce | gallon | pound | quart |

_____

_____

🌀 Now list your own set of words and explain how the words are alike.

_____

_____

_____

WRITING SKILLS

Pretend you work for a chemical company. You have to explain to the Senate committee why you think chemicals should be used. Tell why chemicals are needed and how they help people. First, write down some key ideas. When you have finished your paragraph, proofread your writing. Check it for correct spelling, grammar, capitalization, and punctuation.

Key ideas

- _____
- _____
- _____

Why Chemicals Should Be Used

_____
_____
_____
_____
_____
_____
_____
_____
_____
_____
_____
_____
_____
_____
_____
_____
_____
_____

Rachel Carson will also speak before the Senate committee. Pretend you are Rachel Carson. Explain why chemicals are so dangerous. First, write down some key ideas. When you have finished your paragraph, remember to proofread your writing. Check it for correct spelling, grammar, capitalization, and punctuation.

Key ideas

⚷ _____

⚷ _____

⚷ _____

Why Chemicals Should Not Be Used

_____

_____

_____

_____

_____

_____

_____

_____

_____

_____

_____

_____

_____

_____

_____

_____

_____

_____

_____

LUDWIG VAN BEETHOVEN
1770–1827

Think about It ....

Describe an outstanding musician you have heard about or know.

_____

_____

AS YOU READ Put a ★ beside two important ideas in the story. Then write in the margin why each idea is important.

NOTES

In 1802, thirty-two-year-old Beethoven seemed to have everything—attention, praise, and money. Just ten years earlier he had moved from his home in Bonn, a town in western Germany, to Vienna, which at that time was the capital of the musical world. Joseph Haydn, who was then considered the most famous living composer, had suggested that Beethoven come to Vienna. While passing through Bonn, he had heard Beethoven perform and had seen some of the musical pieces he had written. Haydn was impressed.

Carrying letters of introduction from important people in Bonn, Beethoven quickly dazzled the music-loving, **noble** families of Vienna with his skillful piano playing. People were eager to hear him because his playing was completely different from anything they had ever heard. The Viennese were used to a smooth style of playing. When Beethoven played, however, the piano produced a sound as full as an entire orchestra. He held his hands high and smashed the piano, sometimes breaking strings. Because he wanted the sound to be more powerful, he asked the piano makers to build a better instrument. He complained that those made in Vienna sounded as thin and light as a harp. Beethoven was one of the first modern piano artists. He received attention as rock stars do today. Before him, pianists had pleased the audience, but Beethoven's powerful playing thrilled them.

The Viennese were also beginning to notice his compositions. In 1801, his first string quartets were published. From the beginning, Beethoven's pieces were remarkable for their driving rhythm and vigor. Moody and full of surprises, they seemed to test the limits of the instruments for which they were composed. Many of the rich noblemen had their own orchestras and wanted their musicians to play Beethoven's music. When a few noblemen worried that he might move to another country, they offered him money to stay in Vienna. Beethoven was not ashamed to take the money; he thought he deserved it. Writing to an old friend, Beethoven said that he could tell publishers how much he wanted to receive for a piece of music and they would pay.

At that time, musicians were not thought of as artists or people with great gifts. Instead, they were considered skilled craftsmen, workers who supplied a **product**. Musicians were expected to eat with the servants, not with the people who were listening to their music. But Beethoven knew he had a special gift and expected people to do what he wanted. When he was asked to dinner, he was very unhappy if he was not placed next to his host, the place of honor.

Then the worst thing that can happen to a musician happened to Beethoven. He began to lose his hearing. In a letter to a friend, he wrote that his ears were always buzzing, day and night. He continued, "I can say that I am living a **wretched** life because it is impossible to say to people: 'I am deaf.'... I must tell you that in the theater I must get very close to the orchestra in order to understand the actor. If I am a little too distant, I do not hear the high notes of the instruments, the singers, and if I am a little further back, I do not hear at all."

Beethoven was very upset. By this time, he could hear a low conversation but not the words. To stop his hearing loss, he tried every cure he learned about but nothing worked. He continued playing the piano and conducting his own music, but his wild gestures, together with his poor hearing, completely confused the orchestra. Finally, Beethoven let sight take the place of hearing. His eyes followed the bows, and then he could judge the smallest error in **tempo** or rhythm and correct it at once.

Beethoven's concern about his increasing deafness, however, did not stop him from writing music. In fact, he composed more often and the unique character of his work increased. In 1805, his *Eroica* **Symphony** was played for the first time, and the music world was never the same. With its great force, complex harmonies, fierce sounds, and intense funeral march, it was unlike any symphony that had ever been written.

From 1805, Beethoven's work became more and more dramatic, a well-known quality of his music today. Many people did not like what they heard, but Beethoven would not change one note. He believed that he had a gift and that people would learn to accept his music. He was quoted as saying, "If I write a symphony an hour long, it will be found short enough."

During the next seven or eight years, he wrote several masterpieces, but after that he composed much less. He was sick and had become totally deaf. The only way he could communicate with people was by having them write what they wanted to say or ask in a small notebook. Then, he could answer them. During this time, Beethoven did not worry that he was writing less music because he had new ideas in his head. He worked slowly to put them on paper, changing a phrase note by note until he was satisfied with it.

In 1824, Beethoven completed the Ninth Symphony, one of his greatest works. In the final part, both singers and musicians perform the music. The symphony was presented for the first time right after it was composed. There were only two rehearsals before the performance. One of the singers begged Beethoven to lower the high notes, but he refused. He told her that if she could not sing them, she could just leave them out. After the performance, when the audience started clapping, the lead singer turned Beethoven around. He then could see the tremendous applause, which he could not hear.

People thought Beethoven was the greatest composer in the world. They came from all over Europe and England to visit him. When he died after a long illness, it is said that twenty thousand people went to his funeral. They wanted to honor the man who many people believed wrote the most powerful music ever written by one person.

noble – having a high rank or title in a society

product – anything that is made or created

wretched – very unhappy, miserable

tempo – rate of speed

symphony – a long musical work written for an orchestra

LOOKING BACK AT WHAT YOU HAVE READ

Write your answers to the following questions on the lines below. When the question is in bold print, underline the answer in the story, and write the number of the question in the margin. The answer may be in more than one place. Then write it below.

1. Why did Beethoven move to Vienna?

_____

_____

2. **How was Beethoven's playing different from other piano artists?**

_____

_____

_____

3. In what ways was Beethoven treated differently from other musicians?

_____

_____

_____

4. How do we know Beethoven was a brave person?

_____

_____

_____

5. **How was Beethoven's music different from music that had been written before?**

_____

_____

_____

6. Who are some other famous musicians?

_____

_____

WORKING WITH WORDS

Do you remember what **homophones** are? They are words that sound alike but are spelled differently and have different meanings.

Example: *peace* and *piece*
There is *peace* and quiet in the country.
I asked my mother for a *piece* of cake.

See if you can fill in the blanks with homophones. Be sure to read all of the sentences in each group before you write your answers.

Beethoven played with such force that he would _____ the piano strings.

Be sure that the _____ in the car works.

People loved to _____ Beethoven play.

Come _____ and help me lift the box.

People filled all of the _____ in the concert hall.

The sun _____ at six o'clock this morning.

The _____ was thrilled to have Beethoven as a guest.

The museum has a fine collection of _____.

The emperor stepped down from his _____ and greeted Beethoven.

The girl was _____ from the horse.

Beethoven's music had _____ force and drama.

Did you _____ the cheese and serve it with the spaghetti?

Look at the words *chair* and *couch*.

They belong to the same general class or group. Both are pieces of furniture that we sit on. They differ from each other in that a chair is a seat for one person while a couch is a seat for several people.

◎ Now look at the following pairs of words. Write the name of the class or group they belong to. Then write one way in which they are different. Give yourself a bonus point if you can do the last one.

trumpet–piano

_____

_____

Vienna–Boston

_____

_____

bow–stick

_____

_____

symphony–march

_____

_____

BONUS POINT

Have you ever heard of an **analogy**?

In an analogy, you are trying to figure out the connection between two pairs of words.

Example: Composer is to symphony as author is to _____.

First, you must understand the connection between the words in the first pair, composer/symphony. Make a picture in your mind of these words. Think how they are related. Then make a sentence describing what you see.

A composer *writes* a symphony.

Now use the word you have pictured to make the same connection between the second pair of words. What does an author write?

An author *writes* a book.

The analogy, then, is composer is to symphony as author is to book.

In the following analogies, decide what the connection is between the first pair of words. Make a picture of these words in your mind. Think how they are related. Next, write a word in the blank that will show the same connection between the second pair of words.

Ludwig van Beethoven is to composer as Michael Jordan is to _____.

Concert hall is to symphony as theater is to _____.

Eroica is to symphony as bluejay is to _____.

Beethoven is to Mozart as Beverly Cleary is to _____.

Orchestra is to conductor as class is to _____.

Ear is to hearing aid as eye is to _____.

Admired is to respected as powerful is to _____.

WRITING SKILLS

Beethoven was a very talented person. Write a paragraph about someone you know who you think has a special talent. Be sure that your paragraph has a title, a topic sentence, which gives the main idea of the paragraph, and a concluding sentence, which lets the reader know that you have finished your discussion.

First, write down some key ideas. When you have finished your paragraph, proofread your writing. Be sure to check it for correct spelling, grammar, capitalization, and punctuation.

Key ideas

○— _____

○— _____

○— _____

Title:

_____

_____

_____

_____

_____

_____

_____

_____

_____

_____

_____

_____

_____

_____

_____

_____

_____

Imagine that you are a music teacher and that you want your students to know about Beethoven. Write a paragraph about Beethoven's life. Do not forget to give a title to your paragraph.

First, write down some key ideas. When you have finished your paragraph, proofread your writing. Check it for correct spelling, grammar, capitalization, and punctuation.

Key ideas

🔑 _____

🔑 _____

🔑 _____

Title:

_____

_____

_____

_____

_____

_____

_____

_____

_____

_____

_____

_____

_____

_____

The GREAT BARRIER REEF

Think about It . . . .

How do living things depend on each other?

_____

_____

AS YOU READ Put a ✓ next to parts of the story that you find interesting. Put a **?** next to parts of the story you do not understand.

NOTES

Many people think that in all the seas of the world there is nothing as amazing as the beautiful Great Barrier **Reef** region, the largest group of **coral** reefs in the world. Located off the east coast of Australia, it is half the size of Texas. This huge group of reefs is more than 1,250 miles long and in some spots is 50 miles wide. What is almost impossible to imagine, though, is that the Great Barrier Reef is not made up of one unbroken wall of coral but of more than 2,900 single coral reefs all growing very close together. Except at the lowest tides, most of the reef is below the water's surface. To see it, people either snorkel, scuba dive, or ride on glass-bottomed boats.

The Great Barrier Reef is a finely built **ecosystem** supporting zillions of tiny sea animals called polyps. Just a few millimeters in size, a polyp is a jellylike blob with a mouth surrounded by **tentacles.** It is closely related to the jellyfish. By producing lime, these polyps make their own hard, tube-shaped surface. This is coral, which may be just one polyp or many hundreds joined together in a colony. While some coral reefs grow quickly, others increase in size very slowly and live to be hundreds of years old.

When polyps die, their coral surfaces, which are called skeletons, remain. New polyps then grow on top of these skeletons. Because polyps have been building on top of skeletons for thousands of years, the Barrier Reef is 1,640 feet thick in some places. When polyps are alive, their coral skeletons are beautiful colors, but when they die, they turn white. Every coral reef has two parts, a white base made up of the bodies of billions and billions of polyps that have died over thousands of years, and on top of this a colorful section, formed by living polyps.

Whether people are swimming underwater, sitting in a boat, or just walking, the first thing they see on the Barrier Reef is the colorful coral. In fact, there are four hundred different types of coral on the reef. There is great variety in size, color, and shape. One can see beautiful, underwater coral forests in the form of fans, antlers, or plates. For proper growth, coral needs shallow, salty water that is warm and clean. The water needs to move and receive plenty of light. Because the outer edge of the Great Barrier Reef has these almost perfect conditions, the coral thrives there, and the viewing is impressive.

Coral does not survive above water, but it can provide a habitat for other creatures. Pieces of dead coral and coral sand often build up inside a reef and rise above the water level. Over time, grass starts to grow on this dead coral, which attracts many kinds of birds. Twenty-four species of seabirds live on the reef, and more than two hundred species visit it. Birds carry seeds to these raised areas, or islands. Shrubs and trees start growing from these seeds. In the Barrier Reef region, there are some nine hundred of these islands.

The Great Barrier Reef, which shelters countless plants and animals, is the richest sea **resource** in the world. Twelve thousand dugongs, or sea cows, and twenty-six different types of whales and dolphins swim in the water. Four thousand different kinds of mollusks, such as clams, snails, and oysters, and well over fifteen hundred species of fish live there. Reef fish come in a great variety of shapes and colors. Many have vivid bands, spots, or patches, which help to break up their outline and confuse their enemies. Some can change their color to match their surroundings.

Other fish live in the reef because they have close ties with larger creatures. The cleaner wrasse, a small striped fish, cleans the skin, mouth, and gills of larger fish. Eels and huge manta rays also take advantage of this service. Certain fearless types of fish live within the poisonous tentacles of the giant anemone in complete safety. In some areas, giant groupers grow up to ten feet in length and weigh almost nine hundred pounds. They seem almost tame as they swim with divers and wait to be fed.

In spite of its great size and old age, the Great Barrier Reef is very sensitive and can be destroyed. Since the 1960s, the crown-of-thorns starfish has been eating and destroying the coral reefs. Because the reefs support a wide range of sea creatures, as well as many kinds of birds, their destruction would seriously affect the survival of this sea and bird life. The Australian government is trying to find ways to control the starfish. Another more recent problem for the Barrier Reef is the rapid whitening of the reefs. Scientists think this may have been caused by the rise in water temperature.

Human beings are also causing damage. More than two million people visit the Great Barrier Reef each year. When they walk on the coral or drop anchors on these structures, they cause harm. Even the sweat and suntan lotion in the water from many swimmers and divers can have a negative effect on the fragile reef environment. To preserve it, the Australian government has strict laws. Fishing is allowed in certain limited areas, and animals such as whales, dolphins, green turtles, and dugongs cannot be killed. Taking or damaging any part of the Barrier Reef is a crime, so visitors are asked to take home only photos and memories from this great natural wonder.

reef – a ridge of sand, rock, or coral that lies at or near the surface of the ocean or another body of water

coral – a hard substance like stone, which is made up of the skeletons of tiny sea animals

ecosystem – a community of different plants and animals living together

tentacle – a long, thin body part of certain animals

resource – a supply that can be drawn on

LOOKING BACK AT
WHAT YOU HAVE READ

Write your answers to the following questions on the lines below. When the question is in bold print, underline the answer in the story, and write the number of the question in the margin. The answer may be in more than one place. Then write it below.

1. **What are some amazing facts about the Great Barrier Reef?**

_____

_____

_____

2. **How is a coral reef formed?**

_____

_____

_____

3. **What threatens the Great Barrier Reef?**

_____

_____

_____

4. In the Great Barrier Reef, how do animals and plants help each other?

_____

_____

_____

5. What do you think would be the most interesting thing to see on the Great Barrier Reef?

_____

_____

_____

6. What do you think the Great Barrier Reef will be like in twenty years? Explain your answer.

_____

_____

_____

WORKING WITH WORDS

What three new words did you learn from this story?

_____   _____   _____

Try to use two of them in sentences.

_____

_____

_____

By now you know that an **antonym** is a word that has the opposite meaning of another word. *Weak* is the antonym of *strong*.

See if you can write an antonym for each of these words. Give yourself a bonus point if you can do more than six.

fragile _____   shallow _____

remain _____   fearless _____

vivid _____   variety _____

tame _____   preserve _____

BONUS POINT

53

Do you remember that a **suffix** is a letter or group of letters that we place at the end of a word or word root to change the meaning? The suffix *-less* means "without."

Example: noiseless
Our steps were *noiseless* in the soft snow.

Can you list three words and then make new words by adding the suffix *-less*?

fear   **fearless**

_____   _____

_____   _____

_____   _____

The suffix *-en* means "to make." Try to think of three words and then make them new words by adding the suffix *-en.*

strength   **strengthen**

_____   _____

_____   _____

_____   _____

WRITING SKILLS

The Great Barrier Reef is a very popular vacation spot. What place do you think is special for a vacation? Write a letter to a friend describing it. Be sure you include many interesting details that will help paint a picture in your friend's mind of your special place.

First, write down some key ideas. When you have finished your letter, proofread your writing. Remember to check it for spelling, grammar, capitalization, and punctuation.

Key ideas

🔑 _____

🔑 _____

🔑 _____

Dear _____,

_____

_____

_____

_____

_____

_____

_____

_____

_____

_____

_____

Sincerely,

_____

You are a reporter for your school newspaper and have just returned from a wonderful vacation on the Great Barrier Reef. You are going to write an article for your paper explaining why it is so important to preserve places like the Great Barrier Reef.

First, make sure that you write down some key ideas. Be sure that your article has a title, a topic sentence, which gives the main idea of the paragraph, and a concluding sentence, which lets the reader know that you have finished your discussion. When you have finished your article, proofread your writing. Check it for correct spelling, grammar, capitalization, and punctuation.

Key ideas

Title:

The SALEM WITCH TRIALS

Think about It ....

Why do you think people sometimes
act in ways that are cruel or unjust?

_____

_____

AS YOU READ   Put a ★ beside two important ideas in the story. Then write in the
margin why each idea is important.

NOTES

One of the strangest, and still very mysterious, events in American history was the Salem Witch Trials. In 1692, in the Massachusetts Bay **Colony**, a group of girls, accused both women and men of witchcraft. Two hundred people were jailed; nineteen were **convicted** and hanged as witches. One man was pressed to death with large stones for refusing to answer innocent or guilty to the charge of witchcraft. Eight people died in prison, and fifty-five confessed to practicing witchcraft because a confession would save their life.

What makes this event even more shocking is that it happened among an educated group of people. Many of the residents of the Massachusetts Bay Colony in 1692 knew how to read. In spite of this, most people in New England still had a strong belief in the supernatural. They thought that the Devil existed and that he could control people. A person who welcomed the Devil's influence was a witch and would then try to hurt other people. Massachusetts was an English colony and, according to English law, the punishment for witchcraft was death.

For people living in Massachusetts, the times were very difficult. The English were at war with France, and the war had spread to New England. Not only were the colonists fighting French soldiers from Canada, they also were fighting Native Americans, who had been armed by the French and were attacking their farms and villages. Besides having a very cold, snowy winter, many people were ill with small-pox, a terrible disease.

One February day, a group of six girls in Salem Village were in the kitchen of the town's Puritan minister, Samuel Parris, listening to his slave Tituba, telling stories of magic from Barbados, her **native** country. The two youngest members of the group—the minister's daughter Elizabeth, aged nine, and her cousin Abigail Williams, aged eleven—began to act oddly. They sobbed loudly, crawled under tables, made weird sounds, and screamed that they were being tortured. Several of the older girls also appeared to be having fits. In the next few weeks, the fits continued and got worse. The girls also had mysterious teeth marks on their arms.

Parris noticed that the girls' behavior was very much like that described in a popular book about witchcraft. Dr. Griggs, the village doctor, examined the girls but could find no physical cause for their behavior. He concluded that they were "under the evil hand," meaning they were bewitched or in the control of a witch. The girls named many people as witches, who were then placed in jail.

By May, the governor set up a court to hear the cases and to make a judgment. At the trials, it was very difficult for the people accused of being witches to prove that they were not. This was because the judges accepted as true whatever the girls said, even though no one else could confirm it.

If an accused person **denied** the charge of witchcraft, the judge could ask the bewitched girl to look at the person and see if this was the one who had **tormented** her. Then to show her suffering, the girl cried out as though in pain, saying she was being pinched or bitten. This was the only proof that was needed. The bewitched girls often said that they could see people in the room who were not there. The girls would describe the actions of these people and would seem to be watching them. The judges accepted these statements, too, as proof of witchcraft. The girls always supported each other when they were being questioned. If one of them became uncertain of what to do or say, another girl would give her a hint.

Most of the accused people lived in Salem Village or Salem Farms—about a thirty-square-mile area with a population of less than one hundred households. As the girls' fame in spotting witches grew, people from other towns wanted them to point out witches in their area. In the neighboring village of Andover, the girls did not know the names of the people living there, but this did not prevent them from identifying witches. They started a touch test. When a girl went into a fit because a witch was supposed to be present, the person suspected of being a witch was ordered to touch the girl. If she became quiet, the person who had touched the girl was believed to be a witch.

Throughout the summer of 1692, seven judges listened to the girls accuse people of witchcraft. Nineteen people were put to death. All had denied the charges. But as the months passed, the people in Salem and the nearby villages and towns became very upset. They argued that anyone could be accused of witchcraft, simply because someone did not like him or her. Some of the colony's leading ministers began speaking out against the evidence that was used at the trials. In the fall, the governor ordered that there had to be some proof in addition to what the girls said. With this change, not one more person was convicted. In 1693, the governor freed all of the people still in jail on witchcraft charges.

Although we still do not know with certainty what led to this frightening time of terror, several ideas have been suggested. Some people say the girls were bored and were only playing a game that got out of control. Others suggest that jealousy between neighbors and the desire to get back at someone for old arguments may have had something to do with it. They say fighting between farmers and villagers for more land may have caused it. Just a few years later, the people of Massachusetts held a day of fasting to show their sorrow for the wrong done by the trials. Ten years after the hangings, one of the judges, Judge Sewall, in a public meeting said that the court was guilty and wanted, "to take the blame and shame of it, asking pardon of men." In 1992, the town of Salem created a memorial for the people who were put to death.

colony – a territory that is ruled by another country

convict – to declare or prove that a person is guilty of a crime

native – born in a particular country or place

deny – to say something is not true

torment – to cause someone great pain or suffering

LOOKING BACK AT WHAT YOU HAVE READ

Write your answers to the following questions on the lines below. When the question is in bold print, underline the answer in the story, and write the number of the question in the margin. The answer may be in more than one place. Then write it below.

1. The judges and ministers involved in the trials were well educated, but were they wise? Explain your answer.

_____

_____

_____

2. For several years before1692, the people in Massachusetts had hard times. Do you think this affected how they felt about the trials? Explain your answer.

_____

_____

_____

3. What would you have done if you had been in the room when Elizabeth Parris and Abigail Williams started acting strangely?

_____

_____

_____

4. **When did people realize that something very wrong was taking place?**

_____

_____

5. **How was the wrong corrected?**

_____

_____

_____

6. Do you think something like the Salem Witch Trials could happen today? Why do you think this?

_____

_____

_____

WORKING WITH WORDS

Look at the following phrases from the story. On the lines, write a sentence using each of the words in bold print. Give yourself a bonus point if you can do more than three.

Example:

more **shocking**

It was shocking to hear about the accident.

a terrible **disease**

_____

_____

her **native** country

_____

_____

weird sounds

_____

_____

denied the charge

_____

_____

were **convicted**

_____

_____

BONUS POINT

Look at the words in white. Then look at the pairs of words below them. The words in white explain the relationship between those pairs. Can you write three additional pairs for each item?

antonym	synonym
innocent–guilty	horrible–dreadful

important characteristic	part to whole
winter–cold	roof–house

Do you remember what an **idiom** is? An idiom is a group of words that have a special meaning. If you do not know the special meaning, you will not understand what a person is saying. In fact, it may sound very silly.

For example, "Once in a blue moon."
This means something that does not happen very often.

Read the explanations of the following idioms. Then see if you can write your own sentence using the idiom.

The idiom "stirring up a hornet's nest" means you are causing a lot of trouble.
When the girls accused their neighbors of witchcraft, they stirred up a hornet's nest.

_____

_____

The idiom "smells fishy" means something strange and suspicious.
As more people were accused of witchcraft, people started thinking that something smelled fishy.

_____

_____

WRITING SKILLS

An **expanded paragraph** is one in which you use several supporting ideas to develop your main idea. To make your meaning clear, you should use **transition words**. These words give the signal that you have finished discussing one supporting idea and are ready to move to the next. Remember that these words are always followed by a comma. Here are some common transition words.

first   second   next   last   finally

Nineteen people were put to death because a group of girls accused them of being witches. What do you think about this event? Write an expanded paragraph explaining how you feel about the Salem Witch Trials. Try to use at least three of the transition words above. Be sure that your paragraph has a title, a topic sentence, which gives the main idea of the paragraph, and a concluding sentence, which lets the reader know that you finished your discussion.

First, write down some key ideas. When you have finished your paragraph, proofread your writing. Check it for correct spelling, grammar, capitalization, and punctuation.

Key ideas

Title:

Pretend you are living in the Massachusetts Bay Colony during the Salem Witch Trials. Write a letter to your cousin in England. Describe what has happened.

First, write down some key ideas. When you have finished your letter, proofread your writing. Check it for correct spelling, grammar, capitalization, and punctuation.

Key ideas

- _____
- _____
- _____

Dear _____,

_____

_____

_____

_____

_____

_____

_____

_____

_____

_____

_____

Yours truly,

_____

FATHER MIGUEL HIDALGO
1753-1811

Think about It....

What do you know about Mexico?

_____

_____

AS YOU READ Put a ✓ next to parts of the story that you find interesting. Put a **?** next to parts of the story you do not understand.

On July 29, 1811, the Catholic Church announced that Father Miguel Hidalgo y Costilla was no longer fit to be a priest and **stripped** him of his priestly clothes. Then the government of New Spain, a part of which later became Mexico, sentenced him to death. Early the next morning in Chihuahua, Father Hidalgo was shot by a firing squad. Today, we remember this brave priest as a person who cared deeply about people. He is often called the Father of Mexico.

In the late 1700s, Mexico was part of New Spain and was ruled by the Spanish king. Spain kept strict control of its colony. Only Spain could provide the goods that people needed, so no foreign ships were allowed to enter her ports. Even books coming from France and the United States were forbidden because they might discuss new ideas of freedom and independence.

About six million people lived in New Spain. From the time they were born, each belonged to one of four social classes. At the top were 15,000 Old Spaniards, people who had been born in Spain but who lived in New Spain. Holding most government jobs and having special rights, these people could do almost anything they wished. Below the Old Spaniards were 600,000 Creoles. They had Spanish parents, but they had been born in New Spain. Even though Creoles often were the richest and best-educated people in the Spanish colonies, Old Spaniards looked down on them. Next in rank came a million-and-a-half mestizos. This was the name for the people who had one parent with Spanish blood and one parent who was native to new Spain. While many mestizos were poor, some were quite rich. Then came the lowest group of the four, the three-and-a-half million native people. Their families had lived on the land from ancient times, long before the Spanish came to rule.

Spain had given its settlers the right to demand taxes or labor from the native people. So even though they could stay on their own land, the native people had to work for the Spaniards. The Spanish forced them to work in mines or on haciendas, which were **plantations** owned by Spaniards or the Catholic Church. They were treated badly. Although they worked long hours, they barely earned enough money to feed themselves. Many times they were told their work was not good enough, and then they were not paid. If they were late when called, they would receive fifty whiplashes as punishment.

Father Hidalgo came from a Creole family and was one of five brothers. He grew up in the state of Guanajuato on a large hacienda where his father worked as a manager. As a young boy, he spent a lot of time with the native people who worked for his father. They taught him farming and how to speak their language. At first, Hidalgo was tutored at home, but when he was twelve years old, he and his older brother Jose went to school in Valladolid. Hidalgo was a bright student and decided to become a priest. He loved music and learned to speak many languages. Because he was so smart, his friends nicknamed him "el Zorro," which means "the fox" in Spanish. Later, both brothers graduated from the College at San Nicolas Obispo in Valladolid.

It was around this time that Hidalgo saw an event he would never forget. The native governor of Patzcuaro, Piedro de Soria Villaroel, angered by the terrible working conditions that the Spaniards forced on his people, organized workers from over four hundred villages. The group marched **boldly** into Valladolid to protest their horrible working conditions. Quickly, the authorities stopped the march, captured the governor, and cut off his head. Hidalgo was deeply shocked by this violence.

After graduation, Father Hidalgo worked for a while as a teacher at the College at San Nicolas Obispo, but in 1792 he became the priest at San Felipe in Guanajuato. Whether they were poor native people or rich Creole landowners, Father Hidalgo welcomed everyone equally to his church. In his home, Father Hidalgo often had musical evenings as well as other gatherings. People from the church and his neighbors knew that he read forbidden books from France and the United States, which talked about people's right to be free. They wanted to hear about these books, and they also wanted to talk about their own problems. Of course, the Spanish authorities disapproved of these meetings.

Hidalgo's brother Jose, who was also a priest, worked in the small village of Dolores. When he died in 1803, Father Hidalgo became the priest there. Although some Spaniards and Creoles came to church, most of the churchgoers were Otomi, the native people of that region.

Father Hidalgo wanted to free the native people from the slave labor they were forced to do in the mines and haciendas. Spending his savings and most of his salary, he set up projects that would create jobs that would **benefit** people for a long time. Even though Spanish law forbade growing silkworms, he bought a small piece of property near the church and hired some Otomi to plant over a hundred mulberry trees on it. These trees would feed silkworms, and the silk from the worms would be spun into silk thread. Cloth was made from this silk.

He showed another group of Otomi how to raise bees so they could make honey and wax and helped them plant grapevines and olive trees. In Dolores, Father Hidalgo set up workshops where he taught the Otomi how to tan hides and make bricks. He also introduced another way of making the pottery that the Otomi had used before the Spaniards came. Not only were all of these items nicer than those made elsewhere, but they were better made and cheaper than what the Spanish **merchants** sold.

The Spanish authorities, however, were very angry. No one was allowed to make and sell the same things that workers made in Spain. Father Hidalgo was breaking the law. In 1807, the civil authorities came and uprooted the mulberry trees. His enemies accused him of opposing the beliefs of the Catholic Church, but he was not punished.

Upset by the continuing cruelty of the Spanish, Father Hidalgo joined a group of men who were plotting to take action in December 1810 for Mexican independence from Spain. When someone told the Spanish about the plot, several members of the group were arrested. Instead of running away, Hidalgo decided to act quickly. On the morning of September 16, 1810, he gathered the members of his church by ringing the church bell in Dolores. From the pulpit of his church, Hidalgo announced Mexico's independence crying out "Long live Our Lady of Guadalupe and death to the Spaniards." Later that day, Hidalgo declared that slavery was ended.

Sixty thousand poor weaponless people followed Father Hidalgo into battle. Thousands of Otomi and mestizos joined him, capturing major cities west of Mexico City. When he reached the gates of Mexico City, the capital, he decided to turn back. Perhaps he did not have enough ammunition or perhaps he feared that many lives would be lost in a battle for the Mexican capital. His followers melted away, and the Spanish army captured Father Hidalgo.

At his trial, after he was told that he would be shot, he was asked if he had anything to say. Father Hidalgo replied, "You may fetch me some candy for the firing squad." The next morning, he was taken to a courtyard at the rear of the jail where he was to be shot. Suddenly, Hidalgo remembered that he had left the candy in his cell and asked a soldier to get it. He gave it out to each of the soldiers who were about to shoot him. Perhaps, it was his way of saying that he forgave them for what they were going to do.

Ten more years passed before Mexico became free. For most Mexicans, Father Hidalgo's name has become the symbol of the independence movement, and September 16, the anniversary of the Cry of Dolores, is celebrated as Mexico's Independence Day.

strip – to pull off

plantation – a large estate or farm where the work is done by laborers who live there

boldly – bravely

benefit – to be helpful to; to be helped by

merchant – a person whose business is buying and selling goods for profit

LOOKING BACK AT WHAT YOU HAVE READ

Write your answers to the following questions on the lines below. When the question is in bold print, underline the answer in the story, and write the number of the question in the margin. The answer may be in more than one place. Then write it below.

1. **What were the four social classes living in New Spain?**

_____

_____

_____

2. **Why do people remember Miguel Hidalgo?**

_____

_____

_____

3. **How did Miguel Hidalgo help the native people of Mexico?**

_____

_____

_____

4. Why did Hidalgo risk his life to help others?

_____

_____

5. When New Spain gained its freedom, many people died. Do you think this could have been avoided? Explain your answer.

_____

_____

_____

6. Miguel Hidalgo asked for candy to give to the firing squad. What do you think about this?

_____

_____

_____

WORKING WITH WORDS

Word Puzzle

⌾ Using the letters in the word *Hidalgo*, see how many small words you can make.

HIDALGO

> Sometimes words have more than one meaning.
>
> **Example:** We **rise** at 7:00 every morning.
>
> In the sentence, *rise* means to get out of bed. *Rise* can also mean to go upward.

⌾ In the following sentences, the word in bold print has one meaning. Write what it is. Then see if you can write down another meaning the word may have.

About six million people lived in New Spain, and there were four social **classes**.

_____

_____

_____

Hidalgo was a **bright** student and decided to become a priest.

_____

_____

People knew he read forbidden books from France and the United States that talked about people's **right** to be free.

_____

_____

_____

He showed another group of Otomi how to **raise** bees so they could make honey and wax.

_____

_____

_____

A **proverb** is a short saying that expresses something that many people believe to be true. "Don't put the cart before the horse!" is a proverb. It means that you need to do things in a sensible order or they will not work. You should not jump ahead.

Explain how Miguel Hidalgo's life is an example of the proverb "Do right and fear no one."

_____

_____

_____

Explain how Mexico's fight for independence is an example of the proverb "No pain, no gain."

_____

_____

_____

WRITING SKILLS

Miguel Hidalgo was a true hero of the native people. Write a paragraph about someone who you think is a hero or heroine. Be sure that your paragraph has a title, a topic sentence, which gives the main idea of the paragraph, and a concluding sentence, letting the reader know that you have finished your discussion.

First, write down some key ideas. When you have finished your paragraph, proofread your writing. Check it for correct spelling, grammar, capitalization, and punctuation.

Key ideas

_____

_____

_____

Title:

_____

_____

_____

_____

_____

_____

_____

_____

_____

_____

_____

_____

_____

_____

_____

_____

_____

Pretend you are Father Hidalgo. You are in prison, but before you die you are allowed to write one last letter to your family. What would you write?

First, write down some key ideas. When you finish the letter, proofread it. Remember to check your letter for correct spelling, grammar, capitalization, and punctuation.

Key ideas

🗝 _____

🗝 _____

🗝 _____

Dear _____,

_____

_____

_____

_____

_____

_____

_____

_____

_____

_____

_____

_____

_____

Fondly,

Father Miguel Hidalgo

The LOUVRE

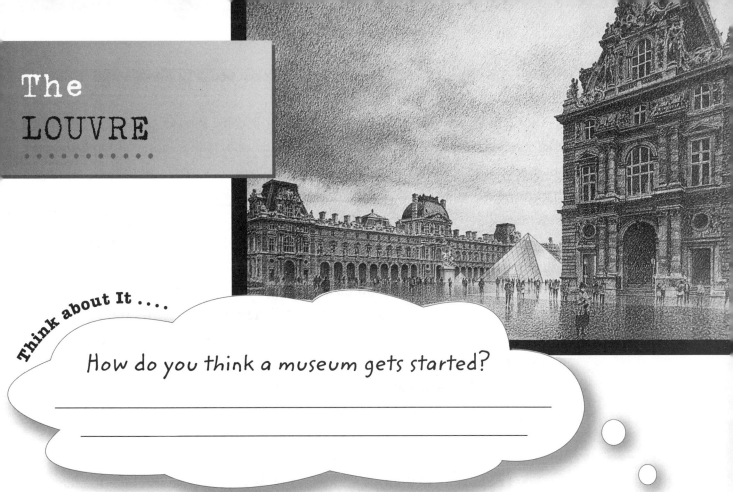

Think about It ....

How do you think a museum gets started?

_____

_____

AS YOU READ Put a ★ beside two important ideas in the story. Then write in the margin why each idea is important.

OTES

The Louvre, which is known today as one of the greatest museums in the world, has existed in different forms in the same place for almost a thousand years. Located in Paris, France, the Louvre is one of the oldest **sites** in the city. It was first built as a castle fortress in 1190 by King Philippe Auguste. It was at the very edge of the city wall, which protected it from its enemies. This castle, now called the Old Louvre, defended the western side of the city. Its **fortified** walls surrounded a large square, which was defended by ten towers and a **moat**. The Great Tower housed the royal treasury and a jail. At the center of this fortress was a huge keep, the strongest, innermost part of the castle. Shaped like a cylinder, the keep was surrounded by another moat. If you visit the Louvre, you can still see part of the keep, the moat, and a portion of the outer wall.

By the late 1300s, a new fortified wall had been built beyond the old wall. The Louvre was no longer needed for defense, so the king, Charles V, decided that he would use it for his palace. He had new windows set into the walls and added stone decorations, statues, and high roofs topped with chimneys. His love of books led him to build a library where he could keep his 973 books, a huge number for one person to own. The printing press had not yet been developed, so all books were written by hand.

The Louvre changed again when Francois I became king in the early 1500s. This king was very interested in the arts and started collecting paintings, sculptures, and other art objects, which he displayed in the Louvre. His works were the start of the Louvre Museum's collection. When Francois decided to make the Louvre his permanent home, he started an **ambitious** rebuilding program. In 1546, a year before his death, Francois I had the keep of the old Louvre torn down and appointed two men to build a grander palace on the site.

The next king, Henri II, continued working to build this new Louvre. His wife, Catherine de Medici, built the Tuileries Palace across the street from the Louvre. This became the main Paris home of the royal family. She also continued construction at the Louvre. At the end of the century, in 1594, Henri IV added another wing to the palace and started work on connecting the Louvre to the Tuileries. When Henri IV died, King Louis XIII continued the construction work at the Louvre, making it bigger and fancier. He bought some art, but the collection remained small.

Only Francois I had thought of the Louvre as his main palace. Yet the other French kings continued adding to it. In the late 1600s, Louis XIV began a major program of rebuilding the Louvre. Then in 1682, he decided to move the French court out of Paris. With the royal family away, the Louvre went into a **decline**. A noisy, messy group of artists and squatters took over its empty apartments. They set up little shacks and shops against its wall.

During his reign, Louis XV planned to tear down the Louvre, which was in poor shape, but then changed his mind and started to repair it. In 1789, the French revolted against their king, Louis XVI. The leaders of the revolution took control of the Louvre. Before King Louis XVI and Queen Marie Antoinette were killed, they spent two years under house arrest in the Tuileries Palace, which was by this time connected to the Louvre.

Louis XVI had planned to start an art museum, but he died before he could do it. The bloody revolution did not put an end to this idea but helped it. In 1793, the new government set up a public museum in the Louvre, belonging to the nation and open to everyone. Though it included only a small selection of paintings from the collection of Louis XVI, people loved it. Just as the Louvre was starting its life as a museum, the new French government was seizing property owned by the church and by noble French families. Most of this artwork was then placed in the Louvre.

When Napoleon became emperor of France at the end of the eighteenth century, he made further renovations. In the 1800s, France would have three more kings and an emperor, Napoleon III. All of them chose to live in part of the Louvre while the other part remained a museum. Two of the kings, Charles X and Louis-Philippe, were thrown out of the Louvre by Paris mobs. During another revolution, in 1871, the Tuileries Palace and part of the Louvre were burned down.

In time, the Louvre became a world-famous museum. As Napoleon I conquered much of Europe, he brought many great paintings and artworks back to Paris and displayed them at the Louvre. Over the years, different French governments added to the Louvre's collection. People also gave art to the museum. There are now 25,000 works of art at the Louvre, including paintings, sculpture, furniture, coins, and jewelry. Visitors are impressed by the museum's amazing painted ceilings and its nine-hundred-foot-long galleries.

In 1981, France's newly elected president, Francois Mitterand, announced that the museum would be remodeled. Through the years, the French government had used space that belonged to the museum for offices. Now Mitterand announced that the Louvre would take back its space. The museum needed a new entrance because the old one could no longer handle the large crowds of visitors. Without asking for a design contest, Mitterand chose the American architect I. M. Pei to be in charge of the project. For the Louvre's major entrance, Pei designed a large glass pyramid. It rises over an escalator and a spiral staircase that take visitors to a lobby below. He also created space underground for museum offices, storage, shops, restaurants, and public parking. Today, the Louvre, which began almost one thousand years ago as a fortress, continues strong and vibrant as one of the most modern and up-to-date museums in the world.

site – the position or location of something

fortify – to make stronger or more secure

moat – a deep, wide ditch that surrounds a castle or town for protection against an enemy; a drawbridge lowered over the moat lets people cross it

ambitious – requiring great ability or effort

decline – to grow less or weaker

LOOKING BACK AT WHAT YOU HAVE READ

Write your answers to the following questions on the lines below. When the question is in bold print, underline the answer in the story, and write the number of the question in the margin. The answer may be in more than one place. Then write it below.

1. **What was in the middle of the fortress?**

_____

_____

2. How do we know that Paris is now very different from when the Louvre was first built?

_____

_____

_____

3. What are some of the changes made to the Louvre over the years?

_____

_____

_____

4. How did the revolution help the museum to grow?

_____

_____

_____

5. Instead of choosing an architect himself, do you think President Mitterand should have had a design contest? Explain your answer.

_____

_____

_____

6. Why do you think I. M. Pei decided to build a pyramid?

_____

_____

_____

WORKING WITH WORDS

Do you remember **synonyms**? A synonym is a word that has the same or almost the same meaning as another word. *Fast* and *quick* are synonyms.

An **antonym** is a word that has the opposite meaning of another word. *Love* and *hate* are antonyms.

Give a synonym and an antonym for each word. The first one is done for you. Give yourself a bonus point if you can fill both columns completely.

start   synonym: _____   antonym: _____

famous   synonym: _____   antonym: _____

center   synonym: _____   antonym: _____

enemies   synonym: _____   antonym: _____

fancy   synonym: _____   antonym: _____

main   synonym: _____   antonym: _____

BONUS POINT

Here are some more similes. You may remember that a simile is a phrase or expression introduced by the two words *like* or *as*. It compares two things that are not alike.

Example: Charles V wanted to feel *as snug as a bug* in his home.

Explain what the simile above means. Then see if you can use it in a sentence.

_____

_____

_____

Now explain what these similes mean and try using them in sentences.

Francois I, who was *as wise as an owl*, was very interested in art.

_____

_____

_____

A person had to be *as tough as nails* to live in the old Louvre.

_____

_____

Do you think I. M. Pei slept *like a log* the night before the opening of the glass pyramid?

_____

_____

How are a pear, an apple, a banana, and a plum alike? If you said that they are all fruits, you are correct. Now read the following sets of words. See if you can add two or more items to each category. Then, write down how they are alike.

tower	
wall	
moat	

gallop	
walk	
trot	

paintings	
drawings	
sculptures	

school	
store	
church	

France	
England	
China	

WRITING SKILLS

I. M. Pei is very proud of the pyramid he designed for the Louvre. Write about something you have done that you are proud of. Be sure that your paragraph has a title, a topic sentence, which gives the main idea of the paragraph, and a concluding sentence, which lets the reader know that you have finished your discussion.

First, write down some key ideas. When you have finished your paragraph, remember to proofread your writing. Check it for correct spelling, grammar, capitalization, and punctuation.

Key ideas

🔑 _____

🔑 _____

🔑 _____

Title:

_____

_____

_____

_____

_____

_____

_____

_____
_____
_____
_____
_____
_____

You have been asked to write a page about the Louvre for a new guidebook of Paris. What would you include in your description? Use details from the story. Be sure that your description has a topic sentence, which gives the main idea of your writing, and a concluding sentence, which lets the reader know that you have finished your discussion.

First, write down some key ideas. When you have finished your paragraph, proofread your writing. Check it for correct spelling, grammar, capitalization, and punctuation.

Key ideas

🔑 _____

🔑 _____

🔑 _____

The Louvre in Paris

_____
_____
_____
_____
_____
_____
_____
_____
_____
_____
_____
_____
_____

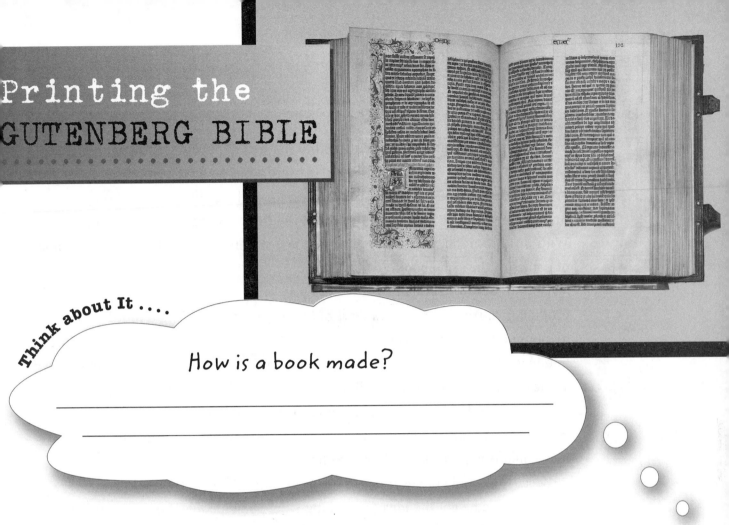

Printing the GUTENBERG BIBLE

Think about It . . . .

How is a book made?

_____

_____

AS YOU READ   Put a ✓ next to parts of the story that you find interesting. Put a **?** next to parts of the story you do not understand.

Until the middle of the 1400s in Europe, only the richest people could afford to buy a book. Each book had to be written by hand because there were no printing presses. A fancy book with beautiful illustrations could take years to make. During the twelfth and thirteenth centuries, many universities were built in Europe. With more people able to read, the demand for books on many subjects increased.

Around A.D. 590, the Chinese had found a way of copying the printed word onto paper by using wooden blocks. By the eleventh century, they were making movable **type** out of clay. Using the movable letters, they could make printed copies of the emperor's laws and orders. Travelers to China brought back the idea of using wooden blocks for printing and the idea of how to make paper. During the early part of the 1400s, craftsmen in Europe printed very simple religious pictures by using a wooden block covered with dark, brown ink. People hung these inexpensive pictures in their homes. Later, craftsmen put several pictures together and produced thin books. In Europe, as in the rest of the world, no one had yet invented a way to produce large numbers of copies of the same book. So the workshops with groups of craftsmen copying books **flourished**.

People realized that they would make money if they could think of another way to copy the same page again and again. They tried to discover an easier, faster way of producing many copies of the same book. One of these people, Johann Gutenberg, a German goldsmith and metalworker, not only developed a printing press but also invented a different kind of ink and a movable metal type. The tiny squares of type, each with a raised letter, were adjusted so that the letters would be evenly spaced on the line to be printed. A narrow letter like *l* needed less space than a wide letter like *w*. A printer could use these movable letters again and again. With this invention, Gutenberg became the first person to produce a large number of copies of the same book.

Born in Mainz, Germany, Gutenberg was living in Strasbourg when he started producing mirrors with frames. Part of the process was making a **mold** into which he poured metal for the frames. Gutenberg sold many mirrors. At that time, large numbers of people took journeys to visit holy **relics**. There were often large crowds at these places, which made it difficult to see the objects. People could hold the mirrors above their heads to get a better view. In addition, they believed that the mirror would capture some of the special power coming from the relic and that they could bring this power home with them.

Because Gutenberg never wrote down his printing methods, we do not know for certain where he got the idea for making type. Some people, however, suggest that it came from his mirror-making. The method for making the frames was very much like the one he used for making movable type. While Gutenberg continued his mirror business, he hired a carpenter to build a wooden printing press. Presses were already used to crush olives and fruit and to flatten and dry sheets of paper. Gutenberg's press was probably a paper press. He invented one part, however, that was brand new. He added a **device** that pressed the paper on to type that was covered with thick ink. His invention was able to prevent the paper from smudging. Gutenberg also developed a new ink because the water-based ink used in woodblock printing ran off the metal type that he was using. His oil-based ink is the earliest example of a modern printer's ink.

In Strasbourg, Gutenberg seems to have realized that his printing method would work. By 1448, he had returned to his hometown of Mainz where he borrowed money to continue work on his inventions. Two years later, records show that Gutenberg borrowed 800 gulden from Johann Fust, a lawyer, "to finish the work." Gutenberg was working on printing copies of the Bible, but he was also continuing to run a printing business. We do not know if he used the same presses, but we do know that at the same time he was working on printing the Bible, he was also printing pieces of paper called papal indulgencies. People bought these from the church. They were supposed to reduce a sinning person's time in Hell. Because so many people wanted them, it was a lot of work to write them out by hand. Gutenberg printed thousands of these papal indulgences. He also printed a thin Latin grammar and a poem.

In 1452, Gutenberg again borrowed 800 gulden from Fust. He wanted to make his printing business bigger. He wanted to set up a workshop that would have several presses, several complete sets of type, and enough workers to work on the presses. This time Fust insisted that he become Gutenberg's partner in the "production of books." Now Gutenberg owed Fust 1,600 gulden or in today's money, well over a million dollars. About 180 copies of Gutenberg's forty-two-line Bible were printed and published around 1455.

Then, Fust demanded that Gutenberg pay back the money he had borrowed, but Gutenberg did not have it. So Fust went to court and received most of Gutenberg's presses as payment. Even though Gutenberg had only a small number of presses, he continued printing. Later, he printed a thirty-six-line Bible. Then sometime after 1460, Gutenberg gave up the printing business. It is believed that he had become blind. In 1465, the archbishop of Mainz made him a "courier," a job where a person is paid but has few duties. Three years later Gutenberg died.

After Gutenberg's success, other people set up printing workshops. When books no longer needed to be written by hand, they could be made much faster. Then the cost of making a book also became much cheaper.

Gutenberg's method of printing was so outstanding that for more than three hundred years, printing remained the same as it had been in his time. Until the end of the eighteenth century, Gutenberg's original design was still thought of as the "common press." His method allowed a person to proofread, edit, and correct the text, which would then be exactly the same in every copy.

Several copies of Gutenberg's forty-two-line Bible still exist in museums and libraries. These are the oldest surviving printed books in the world. When people see a Gutenberg Bible, its beauty and the clearness of its print amaze them.

type – a small piece of metal with a raised letter or number on its surfaces for use in printing; type is coated with ink and pressed onto paper in printing

flourish – to grow with vigor; to develop strongly

mold – a hollow form that is made in a special shape; a liquid or soft material is poured into it to harden into that shape

relic – an object that people believe once belonged to a holy person

device – something made or invented for a particular purpose

LOOKING BACK AT WHAT YOU HAVE READ

Write your answers to the following questions on the lines below. When the question is in bold print, underline the answer in the story, and write the number of the question in the margin. The answer may be in more than one place. Then write it below.

1. **Before Gutenberg's invention of type, how were books made?**

_____

_____

2. What was one problem with making books by hand?

_____

_____

3. **In the late 1400s, why did more people want books?**

_____

_____

4. How did Gutenberg's work with mirrors help him make type?

_____

_____

_____

5. **What were presses used for in Gutenberg's time?**

_____

_____

6. Besides books, what other things are printed by printing presses?

_____

_____

WORKING WITH WORDS

People had many different feelings when they learned the news that Gutenberg printed the Bible on a printing press. Many of them were amazed and delighted. Some were jealous. Think of a time when you heard important news. What was it? Write it down, and then list as many words as you can that describe how you felt. Try to think of at least four.

What was the important news?

_____

_____   _____   _____

_____   _____   _____

Word Puzzle

Using the letters in the word *Gutenberg*, see how many small words you can make. You may use a letter twice in your word if it appears twice in this name.

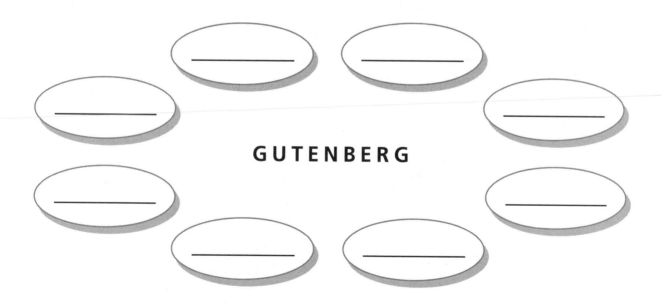

GUTENBERG

A prefix is a letter or group of letters that we place at the beginning of a word or word root to change the meaning. The prefix *re-* means "again."

Example: *recycle*

We can *recycle* these tin cans.

◎ List three words and then make new words by adding the prefix *re-*.

write   **rewrite**

_____   _____

_____   _____

_____   _____

◎ The prefix *under-* means "beneath or under." List three words and then make new words by adding the prefix *under-*.

ground   **underground**

_____   _____

_____   _____

_____   _____

WRITING SKILLS

Draw pictures of four important events in Gutenberg's life. Then write about each picture.

[Drawing box]

_____

_____

_____

_____

[Drawing box]

_____

_____

_____

_____

[Drawing box]

_____

_____

_____

_____

[Drawing box]

_____

_____

_____

_____

Gutenberg's printing press was a wonderful invention. All of us think that certain inventions are useful. Write what invention you think is great and explain why this invention is special. Be sure that your paragraph has a title, a topic sentence, which gives the main idea of the paragraph, and a concluding sentence, which lets the reader know that you have finished your discussion.

First, write down some key ideas. When you have finished your paragraph, proofread your writing. Check it for correct spelling, grammar, capitalization, and punctuation.

Key ideas

- _____
- _____
- _____

Title:

_____

_____
_____
_____
_____
_____
_____
_____
_____
_____
_____
_____
_____
_____
_____
_____

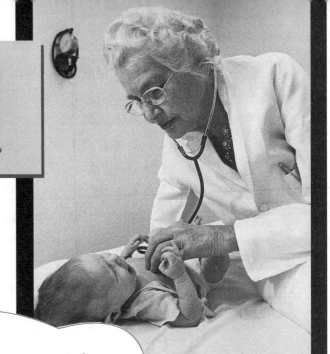

DR. HELEN TAUSSIG
1898—1986

When have you worked very hard for something that was important to you?

_____

_____

AS YOU READ Put a ★ beside two important ideas in the story. Then write in the margin why each idea is important.

NOTES

In the early 1940s, Dr. Helen Taussig thought of a heart operation that saved the lives of thousands of babies who could not receive enough oxygen in their lungs. They were called blue babies. The lack of oxygen gave the babies' skin a blue color. Even those who survived to childhood could not be active and died at a young age. Taussig's **pioneering** work on the heart encouraged other doctors to develop open-heart surgery. Many years later, Taussig explained why her operation "gave a tremendous spurt to heart surgery. When surgeons realized that you could operate on a deeply cyanotic (blue) child, they felt they could operate on almost anyone."

It was not easy for Taussig to become a doctor. She was a child with dyslexia, so reading was difficult for her. To do well in school, she always had to work very hard. Her mother died when Taussig was eleven. Her father, a professor at Harvard College, taught her to be kind and to look at the bright side of things. Taussig went to Radcliffe College, then the women's college at Harvard, and was on the tennis and basketball teams; she transferred to the University of California at Berkeley and graduated in 1921.

Returning home, she thought about becoming a doctor, but in those days, women were not encouraged to enter this field, and many medical schools, including the one at Harvard, did not admit women. Her father urged her to consider working with public health. Yet when Taussig applied to the school for public health, which had just opened at Harvard, she was told that women could study there but would not be given degrees.

So Taussig decided to study medicine in spite of the difficulties women faced. She recalled, "Women were permitted to take some courses at Harvard, but it depended entirely on whether or not the professor wanted to have women in his class." She took two courses. In one, Taussig had to sit by herself in the far corner of the lecture room and was not allowed to speak to any of the male students. When she studied laboratory slides, she had to do it in a separate room. After Taussig finished the second course, the professor told her, "It's foolish for you to be taking these courses here and not getting any credit for them. You should go over to Boston University and get a year of credit."

At Boston University, one of Taussig's professors gave her an ox heart and told her to study the heart muscles. She decided to separate strips of heart muscle and set them up in very salty water. When she ran oxygen through the salty water, the muscles started to beat. Taussig said, "I didn't know it, but others had tried similar experiments with heart muscle and failed. Having no idea it couldn't be done, I just tried and it worked. That was what gave me my start in my work on the heart."

Her professor was very impressed and encouraged her to apply to the outstanding medical school at Johns Hopkins University. Taussig transferred there and graduated in 1927. Throughout the next year, she studied **cardiology**.

In 1927, Dr. Edwards Park came to Johns Hopkins Hospital as head of **pediatrics**. Soon after arriving, he set up a heart clinic for children and appointed Taussig's boss, Dr. Carter, to run it. Taussig also began working there. She enjoyed the children so much that she spent another year and a half studying pediatrics.

Realizing how talented she was, Dr. Park put Taussig in charge of the children's heart clinic in 1930. Taussig thought this was a "golden opportunity" because it combined her two great interests, pediatrics and cardiology. She began her own studies of heart disease in children.

When Dr. Park got a fluoroscope, a new instrument that passed X-ray beams through the body and projected a picture of the heart, lungs, and major blood vessels onto a screen, he told Taussig to learn about heart weaknesses that babies were born with.

Around this time, Taussig became ill with whooping cough, a disease that is now preventable. As a result, she lost part of her hearing. Because of her deafness,

Taussig could no longer use a **stethoscope**, so she gently explored her patients with her hands.

At the clinic, many of the infants Taussig examined were blue babies, but there was no known treatment. Gradually, she realized that most of these babies died because their hearts were shaped in such a way that very little blood, carrying the oxygen, could reach the lungs. She planned an operation that would allow oxygen to enter the lungs. If the operation was successful, the babies would have not only a healthy color but a normal life, too.

Dr. Robert Gross, a **surgeon** in Boston, showed it was possible to tie off a blood vessel that allowed too much blood to reach the lungs. Taussig was very interested in this idea and asked him if he could build a connecting "vessel" to increase the blood circulation to the lungs. He told her that he had built vessels many times, but he was not interested in her idea of trying to develop one for an operation on blue babies. In 1940, Dr. Alfred Blalock, a surgeon, came to work at Johns Hopkins Hospital. He knew how to perform Dr. Gross's operation and was willing to attempt such an operation on a blue baby.

For two years, Dr. Blalock worked on about two hundred dogs to perfect the operation. In 1944, he performed the first operation on a child, but it failed. The second operation was done on an eleven-year-old girl who could not walk across the room without stopping for breath and squatting down. Often she lost consciousness. Her operation was a success. After that, thousands of operations were performed, and eighty percent were successful. The operation became known as the Blalock-Taussig shunt.

Soon the children's heart clinic was flooded with blue-baby patients. Not all of them could be helped, so Taussig's job was to choose those that could benefit from the operation and to take the weakest ones first. After their surgery, she was responsible for their care. Taussig and Blalock developed a team method for dealing with the different stages of blue-baby treatment. It became a model for caring for heart patients as well as for other medical care.

Besides training doctors in the diagnosis and care of children with heart problems, Taussig taught at Johns Hopkins Medical School until she retired in 1963. She also did research on rheumatic fever, the leading cause of heart problems in children. But even after Taussig retired from her clinic and teaching jobs, she continued to be involved in science and medicine. Just before her death at the age of eighty-nine, she had begun to study heart problems in birds.

Taussig, always a warm and caring doctor, never married. She said that she did not have time. As she explained, the only children she ever had were, "the thousands I've taken care of."

pioneering – to be one of the first to develop an area of thought or research

cardiology – the medical study of the functioning and the diseases of the heart

pediatrics – the branch of medicine that deals with the care of infants and children and the treatment of their diseases

stethoscope – the instrument used by doctors and nurses to listen to heartbeats and other sounds in the body

surgeon – a doctor who performs operations

LOOKING BACK AT WHAT YOU HAVE READ

Write your answers to the following questions on the lines below. When the question is in bold print, underline the answer in the story, and write the number of the question in the margin. The answer may be in more than one place. Then write it below.

1. What was so important about Taussig's operation?

_____

_____

_____

2. **Why was it hard for Taussig to become a doctor?**

_____

_____

_____

3. **How did Taussig's professors help her?**

_____

_____

_____

4. Why did Taussig study pediatrics?

_____

_____

_____

5. How do you know that Taussig was a determined person?

_____

_____

6. How was Dr. Park an important figure in Taussig's life?

_____

_____

_____

WORKING WITH WORDS

What three new words did you learn from this story?

_____   _____   _____

Try to use two of them in sentences.

_____

_____

_____

> Here are some more **idioms**. By now you know that an idiom is a group
> of words that have a special meaning. If you do not know the special
> meaning, you will not understand what a person is saying. In fact, it
> may sound very silly. For example, "Straight from the horse's mouth."
> This means to find out some news directly from the person who made it.

Read the explanations of the following idioms. Then write your own sentence, using
the idiom.

The idiom "to take in stride" means to handle unexpected problems successfully.
When Taussig lost most of her hearing, she took it in stride.

_____

_____

_____

The idiom "to open a can of worms" means to start something that may be hard to
stop or control later.
Many medical schools felt if they admitted a woman, they would be opening a can of worms.

_____

_____

_____

Sometimes words have more than one meaning.

Example: They were called **blue** babies.

In the sentence, *blue* means having the color blue.
Blue can also mean unhappy or discouraged.

In the following sentences the word in bold print has one meaning. Write what it is. Then see if you can write another meaning the word may have. Give yourself a bonus point if you can do four or more.

When she studied **slides**, she had to do it in a separate room.

_____

_____

_____

To do **well** in school, she always had to work very hard.

_____

_____

_____

Dr. Carter, the man for whom Taussig was working, would **run** the clinic.

_____

_____

_____

Her father taught her to be kind and to look at the **bright** side of things.

_____

_____

_____

Soon the children's heart clinic was **flooded** with blue-baby patients.

_____

_____

_____

The team method became the **model** for caring for heart patients.

_____

_____

_____

BONUS POINT

94

WRITING SKILLS

An **expanded paragraph** is one in which you use several supporting ideas to develop your main idea. To make your meaning clear, you should use **transition words.** These words give the signal that you have finished discussing one supporting idea and are ready to move to the next. Remember that these words are always followed by a comma. Here are some common transition words.

first   second   next   last   finally

Write an expanded paragraph about Dr. Helen Taussig's remarkable life, using examples from the story for your supporting ideas. Why do you think it was interesting? Try to use at least three of the transition words above. Be sure that your paragraph has a topic sentence, which gives the main idea of the paragraph, and a concluding sentence, which lets the reader know that you have finished your discussion.

First, write down some key ideas. When you have finished your paragraph, proofread your writing. Check it for correct spelling, grammar, capitalization, and punctuation.

Key ideas

- _____
- _____
- _____

Dr. Helen Taussig's Remarkable Life

_____

_____

_____

_____

_____

_____

_____

_____

_____

_____

_____

_____

_____

_____

_____

_____

_____

Taussig had to work very hard at school because she was a person with dyslexia. Write about something that you have difficulty with. Be sure that your paragraph has a title, a topic sentence, which gives the main idea of the paragraph, and a concluding sentence, which lets the reader know that you have finished your discussion.

First, write down some key ideas. When you have finished your paragraph, proofread your writing. Check it for correct spelling, grammar, capitalization, and punctuation.

Key ideas

⊶ _____

⊶ _____

⊶ _____

Title:

_____

_____

_____

_____

_____

_____

_____

_____

_____

_____

_____

_____

_____

MACHU PICCHU

Have you ever found something
important that you did not expect to find?

_____

_____

AS YOU READ   Put a ✓ next to parts of the story that you find interesting. Put a **?** next to parts of the story you do not understand.

OTES

How Machu Picchu, the beautiful Inca city high in the Andes Mountains of Peru, was discovered is an amazing story. In the late 1800s, **archaeologists** started coming to Peru looking for "the lost city of the Incas," known as Vilcabamba. Beginning in the early 1400s, the Inca, a native people of the Andes, had created the largest and most powerful **empire** that South America had ever known. Weakened, however, by a horrible war among Inca chiefs and a terrible disease, probably small-pox, they were conquered in 1532 by a small group of Spanish soldiers, led by Francisco Pizarro. After the Spanish conquered the rest of the land and killed the Inca leaders, some people believed that the last Incas moved to distant Vilcabamba, high up in the mountains, and made it their capital. Because the Inca people had no written language, archaeologists had little information about the location of Vilcabamba. They looked for clues in the writings of sixteenth-century explorers, historians, and mapmakers.

In 1911, Hiram Bingham, a history professor from Yale, organized a group to go to Peru to search for Vilcabamba. They started from Cuzco, a city in the Andes. The group traveled to the small town of Ollantaytambo and set up their headquarters. They looked at a map of the area and asked people if they knew of any **ruins**. They traveled all over the area by mule. Bingham had been warned that a fierce local tribe might attack the group, so they had an armed guard who could speak Quechua, a Peruvian native language.

When the group traveled down a narrow mule trail in the Urubamba **canyon**, they passed a small inn, but they decided to camp by a river. Opposite their campsite was a steep mountain covered with thick jungle. The innkeeper, Melchor Arteagar, came by and Bingham told him they were looking for the palace of the last Inca. Arteagar said there were some excellent ruins on top of two mountains that were opposite each other, the Huayna Picchu, "young peak," and a mountain called Machu Picchu, "ancient peak."

The next morning Bingham offered to pay Arteagar well if he would show him the ruins on Machu Picchu. But it was cold and drizzling, and Arteagar said that it was too hard a climb for such a wet day. Then Bingham offered him a silver dollar; this was three or four times the general daily pay in this area, and Arteagar finally agreed to go. When Bingham asked him where the ruins were, he pointed straight up to the top of the mountain. No one in Bingham's group thought the ruins would be very interesting, so they did not want to go. But Bingham felt it was his job to check out all reports of ruins.

Only Sergeant Carrasco, the armed guard, went with Bingham and Arteagar. Soon they left the main road to walk through the jungle until they reached the bank of a river. A bridge made of six slender logs spanned the narrowest part. If a person fell, he would not live for a moment in the icy cold, rushing water; he would be quickly dashed to pieces against the rocks. Arteagar and Carrasco took off their shoes and crept very carefully across. Bingham remembered, "I got down on my hands and knees and crawled across, six inches at a time." The men passed through a thick jungle, and then they climbed for over an hour up a steep slope. Bingham said, "A good part of the distance we went on all fours, sometimes holding on by our fingernails." It was very humid, and Bingham started thinking that he should not have come.

At noon, when everyone was very tired, they had reached a little grass-covered hut 2,000 feet above the river. Here they met two local farmers, Richarte and Alvarez, who welcomed them with cold water and a few cooked sweet potatoes. The canyon had not been occupied for several centuries, but with the completion of a new government road, settlers were once more moving into the area. On these cliffs 9,000 feet above sea level, the two farmers had found rich soil and plenty of man-made **terraces**.

Bingham learned that the ruins were just a little farther. Everyone but the sergeant and Bingham stayed in the cool shade of the little hut. A small boy was sent to act as a guide for the two men. Very soon Bingham saw a great set of beautifully built stone terraces, perhaps a hundred of them, each hundreds of feet long and ten feet high. A forest of trees had been growing on them for hundreds of years. But farmers had chopped them down and partly burned them to make a clearing so they could grow crops. Doing this was such a big job that the tree trunks were left where they fell. On this trip Bingham had already seen other flights of well-made terraces, so these did not make him very excited.

He continued following the child into the forest. They crawled over terrace walls and through bamboo thickets. Later he wrote, "Suddenly, without any warning, under a huge overhanging ledge the boy showed me a cave beautifully lined with the finest cut stone." On top of this ledge was a rounded temple that looked very much like a famous temple in Cuzco. Bingham thought it was one of the finest examples of stonework he had ever seen. A beautiful wall made of carefully matched pure white stone blocks was connected to this temple. Bingham thought it was "clearly the work of a master artist." This wall and the temple over the cave were "as fine as the finest stonework in the world." Then the little boy said that they should climb a steep hill over a flight of stone steps.

Suddenly, Bingham saw a great stairway of large granite blocks. Then they were in front of the ruins of two of the finest and most interesting structures in ancient America. "Made of beautiful white granite, the walls contained blocks of Cyclopean size, higher than a man. The sight held me spellbound." He had discovered two temples. Bingham thought the lower blocks of stone were about ten to fifteen tons each. Nothing just like them had ever been found. But that was only the beginning. There were two hundred buildings. There were fountains that became small waterfalls, forming a chain of sixteen little baths.

Bingham believed that Machu Picchu was Vilcabamba, the "lost city." Now, we know that in fact Bingham had found Vilcabamba two months earlier but did not realize it. Many archeologists believe that about a thousand people lived in Machu Picchu and that it may have been the center for an area with a large population. Today, more than 300,000 tourists visit Machu Picchu each year. Either coming by an ancient footpath or by train, they marvel at its many terraces that seem endless and its beautiful temples and houses, a perfect spot set high in the Andes Mountains.

archaeologist – a person who studies the way humans lived a long time ago

empire – a group of countries, lands, or peoples under one government or ruler

ruins – what is left after something has been destroyed; the remains

canyon – a deep valley with very high, steep sides, often with a stream running through it

terrace – a raised bank of earth with a flat top and sloping sides

LOOKING BACK AT WHAT YOU HAVE READ

Write your answers to the following questions on the lines below. When the question is in bold print, underline the answer in the story, and write the number of the question in the margin. The answer may be in more than one place. Then write it below.

1. **Why are the Inca remembered?**

_____

_____

_____

2. **Who was Hiram Bingham?**

_____

_____

3. What is so impressive about Machu Picchu?

_____

_____

_____

4. What kind of a person was Hiram Bingham?

_____

_____

_____

5. Why is the discovery of Machu Picchu so amazing?

_____

_____

_____

6. What was important about Bingham's silver dollar?

_____

_____

_____

WORKING WITH WORDS

You remember that a **synonym** is a word that has the same or almost the same meaning as another word. *Happy* and *joyful* are synonyms.

An **antonym** is a word that has the opposite meaning of another word. *Big* and *small* are antonyms.

Give a synonym and an antonym for each word.

horrible	synonym: _____	antonym: _____
conquer	synonym: _____	antonym: _____
fierce	synonym: _____	antonym: _____
slender	synonym: _____	antonym: _____
tired	synonym: _____	antonym: _____
interesting	synonym: _____	antonym: _____
ancient	synonym: _____	antonym: _____

Look at the words in white. Then look at the pairs of words below them. The words in white explain the relationship between those pairs. Can you write three additional pairs for each item?

country and capital	member of a group or class
Peru–Lima	donkey–animal

agent and action	important characteristic
archaeologist–explore	trunk–tree

A **simile** is a phrase or expression introduced by the words *like* or *as*; it compares two things that are not alike.

Example: Bingham was probably *as stiff as a board* after his first day of exploring.

@ Explain what the simile above means. Then see if you can use it in a sentence.

_____

_____

_____

@ Now explain what these similes mean and use them in sentences. Give yourself a bonus point if you can do the last one.

Bingham moved *like a snail* across the bridge.

_____

_____

_____

Bingham was *as red as a beet* by the time he had climbed two thousand feet above the river.

_____

_____

_____

Trying to find Machu Picchu was *like looking for a needle in a haystack.*

_____

BONUS POINT

_____

_____

WRITING SKILLS

Write a paragraph describing Bingham's discovery, using details from the story. Of course, your paragraph will have a title, a topic sentence, which gives the main idea of the paragraph, and a concluding sentence, which lets the reader know that you have finished your discussion.

First, write down some key ideas. When you have finished your paragraph, proofread your writing. Please check it for correct spelling, grammar, capitalization, and punctuation.

Key ideas

- _____
- _____
- _____

Title:

_____

_____

_____

_____

_____

_____

_____

_____

_____

_____

_____

_____

_____

_____

_____

What if you could travel back in time and interview Hiram Bingham? What are four questions you would like to ask him?

_____

_____

_____

_____

Now use these questions and write a "back-in-time" interview with Bingham for your school newspaper. When you have finished your interview, proofread your writing. Check it for correct spelling, grammar, capitalization, and punctuation.

My Interview with Hiram Bingham

_____

_____

_____

_____

_____

_____

_____

_____

_____

_____

_____

_____

_____

_____

_____

_____

WOMEN WORKERS of World War II

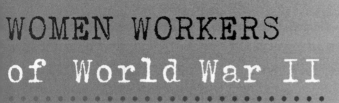

Women in the war

WE CAN'T WIN WITHOUT THEM

Think about It ....

What have you done to help your community or your country?

_____

_____

AS YOU READ   Put a ★ beside two important ideas in the story. Then write in the margin why each idea is important.

NOTES

Today, many women work in interesting, responsible jobs, but this has not always been true. Before the United States entered World War II in 1941, most women had never worked outside of their own home. If they did work, they were not well paid, and they did not have jobs that people respected. The country was still recovering from the Great Depression years, a time when many people were out of work. There had always been **discrimination** against women working, but during the depression, this became much worse. Most people felt that one person's salary should be enough to support a family. Many school districts would not hire married women as teachers, and they would fire them once they did marry. In 1936, eighty-two percent of all Americans said that a wife should not work if her husband had a job.

Even before the United States entered World War II, President Roosevelt thought that the United States should start to get ready. He wanted 50,000 planes to be built; to do this, more workers would be needed. Knowing that there would not be enough men to fill these jobs, the government encouraged companies to hire women, announcing that there were nearly two million women ready to work in defense industries. Still, some employers refused to hire women for highly paid, skilled factory jobs. They said that women were not strong enough, that they did not have the mechanical knowledge, and that they would **distract** the men working there.

The government set up job-training programs for women; one government program taught 20,000 young women such skills as **welding** and radio repair. Eleanor Roosevelt, the president's wife, even wrote the script for a film showing women in a number of roles, including a scientist, a factory worker, and a Red Cross volunteer. By the fall of 1941, many women had started working in defense industries building dive-bombers, turning out millions of rounds of machine-gun and small-arms ammunition, and inspecting aircraft engines.

Many husbands were upset about their wives working in "men's" jobs. When one husband wrote a letter to a newspaper saying, "I don't want my wife to take a man's job as long as I am still able to work for our living," he was expressing what many other husbands felt. But after the Japanese attacked the United States naval base at Pearl Harbor in December 1941 and the country entered the war, the men went off to fight. Then the United States needed women war workers to fill the men's jobs.

In January 1942, President Roosevelt said the country was not producing enough. It needed 60,000 planes, 45,000 tanks, and 20,000 antiaircraft guns. To improve production, automobile plants were changed into aircraft plants, shipyards expanded, and new factories were built. To fill the need for workers in these new and growing industries, the government took complex jobs that formerly had been done by highly skilled workers and broke them down into smaller jobs that could be learned quickly.

Some of the first women to work in these plants were those who had already been working but in low-paying jobs. Many restaurants and laundries were forced to close as their women workers left for more highly paid war jobs. The difference in pay was enormous. For example, in Mobile, Alabama, a waitress earned fourteen dollars a week and a salesperson twenty-one dollars a week, but a shipyard worker earned thirty-seven dollars a week.

In California, Margaret Salazar quit her job in a beauty parlor and took a job in an aircraft plant. She recalled, "The money was in defense. You made more hours, and the more hours you made, the more money you made. And it was exciting.... You figured you were doing something for your country and at the same time making money."

With the promise of new, well-paying war jobs, many people moved to areas of the country that were growing, like the West and the North. One woman, Bethena Morse, moved from Derrider, Louisiana, to Richmond, California. Years later, she said, "After they bombed Pearl Harbor, the next thing you heard was, 'There's ship-building in California.' Anybody could have done what I was doing in Louisiana," she said about her job, which was operating a pressing machine at a laundry. "Building a ship was a different feeling."

Although many working women switched to war jobs, the government and industry needed even more workers. Women who had never worked outside of their home had to be persuaded to take jobs. Not only the women but also their husbands and their new bosses had to be convinced. In addition, the people they would be working with had to get used to the idea of having women coworkers. The government produced posters and photos showing women working in defense jobs. These were designed to encourage women to help the war effort. Newspapers, magazines, and radio stations ran ads and stories asking for more women workers.

"Rosie the **Riveter**," a song telling about a woman war worker came out in 1943. People heard the words everywhere in the United States—on the radio, in bus and train stations, even on coin-operated machines in restaurants.

> *All the day long, whether rain or shine,*
> *She's part of the assembly line,*
> *She's making history working for victory,*
> *Rosie, Rosie, Rosie, Rosie, Rosie, Rosie the riveter.*

Whether she was in a song, on a poster, or on a magazine cover, Rosie became the symbol of all women war workers.

In 1943, *Newsweek* told its readers, that women workers were everywhere. "They are in the shipyards, lumber mills, steel mills, **foundries**. They are welders, electricians, mechanics, and even boilermakers. They operate streetcars, buses, cranes, and tractors." Before the war, bus drivers, hospital workers, police officers, and bank tellers were men; now women were doing these jobs. Even in the arts, there was change. Conductors of symphony orchestras, who before had refused to hire women musicians, saying they did not have the energy or temper to play in an orchestra, now hired women. Before the war, well-trained women doctors found it difficult to get jobs; now they were welcomed.

During World War II, more than six million women joined the workforce. *Time* magazine called the United States wartime production a "miracle." Among other things 296,429 airplanes, 87,620 warships, and 47 tons of ammunition were produced. None of this would have been possible without America's women war workers.

discrimination – an unfair difference in treatment

distract – to draw one's attention away from what one is doing or thinking

welding – joining pieces of metal or plastic by heating until soft enough to be hammered or pressed together

riveter – a person whose job is to fasten pieces of metal together with a metal bolt

foundry – a place where metal is melted and then shaped into different products

LOOKING BACK AT WHAT YOU HAVE READ

Write your answers to the following questions on the lines below. When the question is in bold print, underline the answer in the story, and write the number of the question in the margin. The answer may be in more than one place. Then write it below.

1. **How many women began working during World War II?**

   _____

   _____

2. Why were many men against women working?

   _____

   _____

   _____

3. When World War II started, how did women's lives change?

   _____

   _____

   _____

4. **Why did many women like their war jobs?**

   _____

   _____

   _____

5. Are today's working women different from the women who worked during World War II? Explain why you feel this way.

   _____

   _____

   _____

6. When the war ended, what do you think happened to the women war workers?

_____

_____

_____

WORKING WITH WORDS

How did women workers feel during World War II? Try to think of at least five words that describe how they felt.

_____   _____   _____

_____   _____   _____

_____   _____   _____

Look at the following phrases from the story. On the lines, please write a sentence using each of the words in bold print. Give yourself a bonus point if you can do more than three.

Example:

complex jobs

The complex directions were difficult to understand.

responsible jobs

_____

_____

distract the men working there

_____

_____

discrimination against women working

_____

_____

persuaded to take jobs

_____

_____

variety of jobs

_____

_____

BONUS
POINT

In an **analogy**, you are trying to figure out the connection between two pairs of words.

Example: Factory worker is to factory as waitress is to _____.

First, you must understand the connection between the words in the first pair, factory worker/factory. Make a picture in your mind of these words. Think how they are related. Then make a sentence describing what you see.

A factory worker *works* in a factory.

Now use the word you have pictured to make the same connection between the second pair of words. Where does a waitress work?

A waitress *works* in a restaurant.

The analogy, then, is factory worker is to factory as waitress is to restaurant.

In the following analogies, decide what the connection is between the first pair of words. Make a picture of these words in your mind. Think how they are related. Next, write a word in the blank that will show the same connection between the second pair of words.

Franklin Roosevelt is to president as Babe Ruth is to _____.

Sailor is to navy as soldier is to _____.

Tank is to weapon as earring is to _____.

Laundress is to laundry as mechanic is to _____.

Sick is to ill as excellent is to _____.

Wing is to airplane as rudder is to _____.

WRITING SKILLS

You have just read that during World War II there were newspaper and magazine articles that tried to convince women to join the workforce. See if you can write a story that would make women want to work for the war effort. Remember to give your story a title.

Before you begin, write down some key ideas. By now, you know that you have to proof-read your writing. Check it for correct spelling, grammar, capitalization, and punctuation.

Key ideas

- _____
- _____
- _____

Title:

_____

_____
_____
_____
_____
_____
_____
_____
_____
_____
_____
_____
_____

Many women war workers have said that the war years were very special to them. Why do you think that they felt this way? What was one of your experiences that has had a big effect on you? Why was it so important? Write a paragraph about your experience. Remember your paragraph should have a title, a topic sentence, which gives the main idea of the paragraph, and a concluding sentence, which tells the reader that you have finished your discussion.

First, write down some key ideas. When you have finished your paragraph, please proofread your writing. Of course, do not forget to check it for correct spelling, grammar, capitalization, and punctuation.

Key ideas

- _____
- _____
- _____

Title:

_____

_____

_____

_____

_____

_____

_____

_____

_____

_____

_____

_____

_____

_____

_____

_____

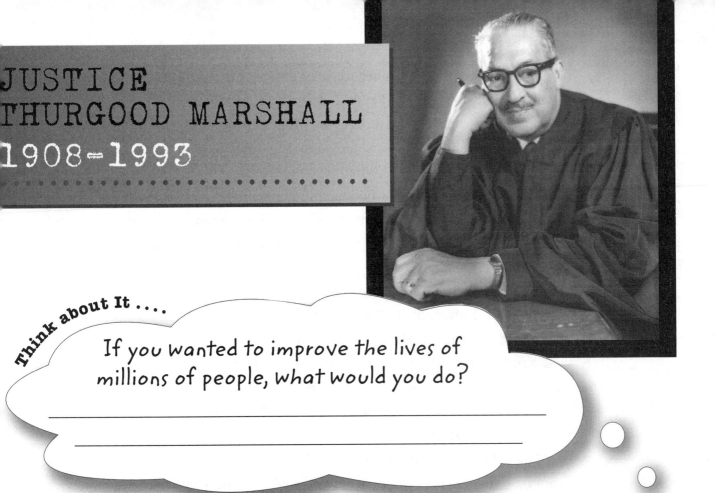

JUSTICE THURGOOD MARSHALL 1908–1993

Think about It . . . .

If you wanted to improve the lives of millions of people, what would you do?

_____

_____

AS YOU READ Put a ✓ next to parts of the story that you find interesting. Put a **?** next to parts of the story you do not understand.

NOTES

What did Thurgood Marshall want? He wanted African Americans to have the same chance in life as white people. Marshall wanted to end **segregation** in the United States. But for this to happen, old laws had to be changed, and new laws had to be made. All of his adult life, first as a lawyer and then as a judge, he worked to reach this goal.

Marshall's family were proud people who spoke out for equal rights for African Americans. Marshall's mother was a teacher, and his father worked as a waiter on a railroad train. His father told his son that he would have to fight his own battles. Marshall recalled his father telling him, "Son, if anyone ever calls you 'nigger,' you not only got my permission to fight, you got my orders to fight him."

Marshall grew up in Baltimore and often got into trouble at school. His teacher had an unusual method of discipline. Years later, Marshall remembered, "Instead of making us copy out stuff on the blackboard after school when we misbehaved, our teacher sent us down into the basement to learn parts of the Constitution. I made my way through every paragraph." Marshall says that doing this gave him a life-long respect for the highest law of our land.

When it came time for college, sixteen-year-old Marshall decided he wanted to go to Lincoln University in Pennsylvania, the only college for African-American young men on the East Coast. Because his family did not have the money to pay for his college education, Marshall worked full-time as a dining-car waiter on the Baltimore & Ohio Railroad. When he complained that his uniform was too small, the headwaiter told him that finding another waiter would be easier than finding another pair of pants. He advised Marshall to just "scroonch" down in them. After working for six months, he had saved enough money to pay for his first year at Lincoln.

In 1930, after graduating from Lincoln with honors, Marshall applied to the law school at the University of Maryland. The school would not admit him because he was African-American. Marshall was furious. After all, he lived in Maryland and was a fine student. He decided to go to Howard University Law School, an African-American school in Washington, D.C. By then, the United States was in the Great Depression, and many people were out of work. His mother helped him pay the entrance fee by **pawning** her wedding and engagement rings.

Marshall could not afford to live in Washington, so he **commuted** every day from Baltimore. During the train ride he studied; soon he was the best student in his class. Because he was such a fine student, the school gave him a job in the law library. The money he earned helped pay for his schooling. He also started working for Charles Houston, an outstanding African-American lawyer and a wonderful law professor. Houston told his students to use the law to fight everyday conditions, practices, and rules that were not giving African Americans an equal chance.

After Marshall finished law school in 1933, he opened a law office in Baltimore. The Great Depression continued. Marshall found himself working on civil rights cases for poor **clients**. Often they could not afford to pay him, but he was winning the cases.

Meanwhile, his professor Charles Houston had become the chief lawyer for the National Association for the Advancement of Colored People (NAACP), a group that worked for equal rights for African Americans. In the South at that time, all of the schools were segregated. Even though the education was separate, it was supposed to be of equal quality. Since he did not have many clients, Marshall went with Houston when he visited schools that were segregated. Often, the schools were no more than shacks. Sometimes they could see the sky through the many holes in the roof. Houston talked with Marshall about how important integration was. He explained that only when African Americans and whites got the same chances in life could there be equal rights.

Marshall became the lawyer for the Baltimore branch of the NAACP. In 1935, he worked on a case that resulted in the University of Maryland Law School being ordered to admit its first African-American student. This was the same school that had rejected his application in 1930.

A year later, Houston hired Marshall to work on his law team in New York. Then in 1938, when Houston left the NAACP, Marshall took over his job as chief lawyer. The two continued working together closely. They decided to use the courts to make sure that African Americans were given their full rights as citizens. They won more and more cases. At first, the NAACP asked only that African-American schools be as well equipped as white schools. But then, Marshall convinced the NAACP to change its **approach**. He argued that the NAACP should handle only cases that would change the laws of segregation itself.

In 1954, Marshall and the NAACP had their greatest victory when they took the case of *Brown v. Board of Education* before the Supreme Court, the highest court in the United States. Arguing that the Constitution forbids segregation, Marshall said that the "separate but equal" segregation plan that twenty-one states had in their public schools was not fair. When one of the justices asked him what he meant by "equal," Marshall said, "Equal means getting the same thing, at the same time, and in the same place."

When the Chief Justice of the Supreme Court, Earl Warren, announced the court's decision, he said that "separate but equal has no place" in public education. Marshall recalled that when he heard these words, "I was so happy I was numb."

Wanting to help his country even more, Marshall accepted President Kennedy's offer in 1961 to become a federal judge. Six years later he became a justice of the Supreme Court and was the first African American to hold this position.

At the age of eighty-three, after serving on the Supreme Court for twenty-four years, Marshall resigned. His health was getting worse. A year later he died.

At the funeral, Chief Justice Rehnquist reminded people of the words that are above the entrance to the Supreme Court, "Equal Justice Under Law." Then he said that no one person had done more to make these words come true than Thurgood Marshall.

segregation – the practice of separating one racial group from another

pawn – to leave something valuable with a lender of money in order to get a loan

commute – to travel regularly to and from work or school over quite a long distance

client – a person or organization that uses the services of another person or organization

approach – a method of doing something

LOOKING BACK AT WHAT YOU HAVE READ

Write your answers to the following questions on the lines below. When the question is in bold print, underline the answer in the story, and write the number of the question in the margin. The answer may be in more than one place. Then write it below.

1. What do you think of the punishment that Marshall's teacher gave to him? Explain your answer.

_____

_____

_____

2. In what ways did segregation affect both African Americans and whites? Explain your answer.

_____

_____

_____

3. **How do you know that Marshall's mother thought his education was very important?**

_____

_____

4. How do you think Marshall felt when the University of Maryland Law School admitted its first African-American student? Explain your answer.

_____

_____

_____

5. How did Charles Houston affect Marshall's life?

_____

_____

6. Why was the case of *Brown v. Board of Education* so important?

_____

_____

_____

WORKING WITH WORDS

Word Puzzle

Using the letters in the word *Thurgood*, see how many small words you can make. You may use a letter twice in your word if it appears twice in this name. Give yourself a bonus point if you can think of more than eight.

THURGOOD

BONUS POINT

> Remember idioms? An **idiom** is a group of words that have a special meaning. If you do not know the special meaning, you will not understand what a person is saying. In fact, it may sound very silly. For example, "To throw in the towel." This means to quit or to give up without winning.

Read the explanations of the following idioms. Then write your own sentence using the idiom.

The idiom "to give someone the cold shoulder" means to show someone he is not welcome. When Thurgood Marshall wanted to study at the University of Maryland Law School, he was given the cold shoulder.

_____

_____

The idiom "bite off more than one can chew" means trying to do more than you have the time or ability to do.

When Marshall decided to try to end the segregation laws, some people told him, "Don't bite off more than you can chew."

_____

_____

The idiom "feel like a million dollars" means that a person is feeling very happy.

Thurgood Marshall must have been feeling like a million dollars after he heard the *Brown v. Board of Education* decision.

_____

_____

Of course, you remember that a **definition** explains the meaning of a word or group of words. A definition of the word *waiter* is a man whose job it is to serve food or drink in a restaurant or other place.

@ Write a definition for the following words.

equal rights

_____

_____

shack

_____

_____

reject

_____

_____

numb

_____

_____

WRITING SKILLS

Draw pictures of four important events in Thurgood Marshall's life. Then write about each of them.

_____
_____
_____
_____

_____
_____
_____
_____

_____
_____
_____
_____

_____
_____
_____
_____

An **expanded paragraph** is one in which you use several supporting ideas to develop your main idea. To make your meaning clear, you should use **transition words.** These words give the signal that you have finished discussing one supporting idea and are ready to move to the next. Remember that these words are always followed by a comma. Here are some common transition words.

first   second   next   last   finally

What events did you find interesting in Marshall's life? Write an expanded paragraph explaining why you find these events so interesting. Try to use at least three of the transition words above. Be sure your paragraph has a title, a topic sentence, which gives the main idea of the paragraph, and a concluding sentence, which lets the reader know that you have finished your discussion.

First, write down some key ideas. When you have finished your paragraph, proofread your writing. Check it for correct spelling, grammar, capitalization, and punctuation.

Key ideas

_____

_____

_____

Title:

_____

_____

_____

_____

_____

_____

_____

_____

_____

_____

_____

FINAL ASSIGNMENT

Make a time line. Place in order at least twelve of the people, places, and events presented in these fifteen stories. Draw pictures, if you wish, to go with some of the dates you marked.

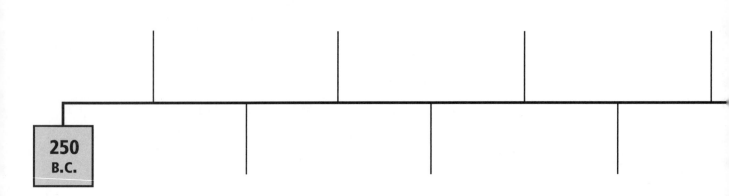

250 B.C.

A.D.
2000

Image Credits

- Page 1: *The Empire State Building*
  Photo by Lewis Hine, courtesy of the New York Public Library

- Page 9: *Conquering Mount Everest*
  Courtesy of the Royal Geographical Society, London

- Page 17: *Queen Elizabeth I*
  Courtesy of the National Portrait Gallery, London

- Page 25: *The Great Wall of China*
  PhotoDisc © 2001

- Page 33: *Banning DDT*
  Bettman/Corbis

- Page 41: *Ludwig van Beethoven*
  Portrait by J. W. Mahler, courtesy of the Gesellschaft der Musikfreunde, Wien

- Page 49: *The Great Barrier Reef*
  Courtesy of the Great Barrier Reef Marine Park Authority

- Page 57: *The Salem Witch Trials*
  Courtesy of the Peabody Essex Museum

- Page 65: *Father Miguel Hidalgo*
  © Schalkwijk, courtesy of Art Resource, New York

- Page 73: *The Louvre*
  Courtesy of Pei Cobb Freed & Partners Architects LLP, New York

- Page 81: *Printing the Gutenberg Bible*
  © The Pierpont Morgan Library, courtesy of Art Resource, New York

- Page 89: *Dr. Helen Taussig*
  Courtesy of Johns Hopkins Medical Institutions, the Alan Mason Chesney
  Medical Archives, Baltimore, and of Tadder Associates, Inc., Baltimore

- Page 97: *Machu Picchu*
  PhotoDisc © 2001

- Page 105: *Women Workers of World War II*
  Courtesy of Library of Congress, LC-USZ62-111835

- Page 113: *Justice Thurgood Marshall*
  Photo by Hessler Studios, courtesy of the Collection of the Supreme Court of
  the United States, Washington, D.C.